Dedicating Your Life to Spirit

by wah!

I don't want to talk about long ago. I want to talk about now. What's going on in your life *now*? What do you dedicate yourself to? I dedicate myself to spirit.

The basis for my work is evolution of the soul. Through yoga, chant, introspection and self-awareness, I have been able to enhance my purpose. I am a very thirsty soul. I really want to know what inspires people to grow. Intense study, intense practice, humor, and kindness are integral parts of my personal evolution.

I hope sharing my life will help open yours.

wah*!*

all photos by Ekongkar, except photo on p. 83 taken by Jeanny Tsai © 2005

design and layout by Cheryl Albrecht - www.cherylalbrecht.com

studio photos taken at Mukti Yoga Studio, Manhattan Beach, CA

yoga classes contained in book use abbreviations for added clarity
- L is left, R is right.

table of contents

wah! yoga ~ self-healing

self-examination ~ roles we play

chanting ~ singing your heart out

Build the Self from within.

WAH! YOGA

self-healing

I am a musician by profession. Most people know me from my CD's and concerts, which are based in a meditative practice known as chanting. For me, chanting, meditation and yoga have always been intertwined. It seems perfectly natural to chant, practice yoga and meditate all in the same day. In this book, I share the practices which I have found useful in processing change in my own life - cleansing the body and mind through yoga, embracing the divine through chanting, and processing my life decisions and karmas through intense self-examination.

Most people are familiar with my music. The liner notes of my CD's tell stories and offer explanations of the mantras. Many people have asked for the spontaneous *dharma* talks from my concerts so I have included these here as well as more specific information about life processing, singing, mantras and meditation.

The yoga I teach is an amalgamation of what has worked for me through many phases of my life – youth, pregnancy, birth, growth, sickness, health and exhaustion. I have investigated these practices through research and study, through experimentation, and through teaching students who have various impairments. Many of the variations you will find in this booklet are a result of sharing and experimentation. And yet the basic teachings of yoga are unchanged, outlined by sacred texts such as the *Gherand Samhita* and *Hatha Yoga Pradipika*. I have not created something new. Yoga is ancient and complete. However, what I have done is combine them differently according to my needs. My unique combination of these practices is what I share, encouraging others on the path to spiritual awakening.

My practice is based on healing from the inside out. Visualization and inner changes happen long before any of it actually manifests in our lives. I have found it necessary to concentrate fiercely on the inner world. This is my center of gravity, my dispatch center, my center of operation.

Learning the real methods of yoga takes many years. Practice, intense study and searching will give you the tools you need. For the first ten years of teaching, I taught "by the book" and never wavered from the original teachings I was given. But gradually the structure fell away and I started teaching from a place of consciousness I didn't realize I had. In a meditative state, I could ask the void for guidance and channel teachings I knew or which came directly from the void. At first, this method felt precarious. I didn't feel I had permission to depart from the original teachings, but neither could I stop my own expansion. My students and I both felt a spaciousness and sense of love when I taught from this place.

As I came forward as a teacher, I also evolved personally. Aspects of my personality were incorporated into my teaching style. I am intensely focused on inner growth. I am also very playful. I love witty games, children's activities, play-acting, and role playing. As I came forward as a teacher, these aspects naturally embellished my teaching style. The classes became as much about *asana* as they were about laughing, breathing, and playing games. Playful exploration of the poses became a pillar of my practice. I found childlike innocence helpful in creating a pure energy within myself. Many adults I met had layers of conditioning, training, and disappointment built into their skeleto-muscular system which impaired their posture, breathing and inhibited their overall energy. I taught yoga to children for seven years in a summer camp, and their games and childlike approach to postures were useful in breaking up static adult energies. Mimicking their spontaneous games and movements gave my students a chance to operate differently - with free-flowing energy and in an uninhibited way. I had to get them to let go of their old habit patterns before I could ask them to realign mind and body with spirit.

My classes were filled with a wide range of physical ability. Some students were physically active and others were handicapped, overweight, or injured. Everyone who came was trying to process what was going on in their lives. I had one student who practiced with me once a week for many years. Over a twelve-month period, he had knee pain, swelling, and surgery, followed by several months of healing. Then he broke the opposite ankle and came to class for three months with a cast on his leg. Working with him forced me to find new ways to move the energy and develop core strength. I also had a blind woman attend classes. She was faithfully accompanied by her seeing eye dog, who napped and snored at the edge of her yoga mat. I needed to teach postures that were appropriate for sighted and blind students alike. So many types of people came. Injuries needed to be healed, grief needed to be comforted, sadness needed to be released. I searched for yogic movements that would be effective for the widest range of people with or without handicaps.

My yoga style combines three basic schools of yoga - Anusara Yoga, Bihar Yoga, and Children's Kundalini Yoga. Anusara Yoga developed by John Friend, is unparalleled in its examination of alignment, step-by-step instructions for creating postures, and understanding energetic flows in the body. All Anusara-certified teachers complete a rigorous program of study. Besides being a knowledgeable group of people, it is also a wonderful heart-centered community. The Kundalini yoga I taught to children (founded by Yogi Bhajan) was a good precursor to Bihar Yoga, which explored similar teachings but in greater detail.

Anusara Yoga
www.anusara.com

Bihar Yoga
www.yogavision.net
www.satyananda.net
www.scand-yoga.org

For further study, I recommend the following - for asana, alignment, strengthening and any injuries study Anusara Yoga. For detailed systems of pranayama, meditation, mudra, and self-cleansing study Bihar Yoga. For moving postures, coordinating movement and breath, explore Kundalini. I have added to this various self-massage and self-healing techniques I have gathered from healers. Combined together, this is a unique practice which just about anyone of any age or ability can do, and which will be effective in dissolving energetic blockages in your body, mind and life.

how to use this book

Section I: YOGA   Section II: SELF-EXAMINATION   Section III: CHANTING

The first section (YOGA) attempts to introduce you to my basic approach to yoga. There was no way to include all of what I teach. The classes are presented at a beginning-intermediate level, with suggestions for more challenge. Where possible, I give instructions for the poses in sequential order; if the next instruction is too difficult, revert to the previous form. For example, in backbend, you can hold bridge pose (easy), bring the top of the head on the floor and melt the heart (intermediate), or lift the heart and come up into backbend (difficult). Each step strengthens and leads to the next. Do what feels comfortable. The postures should feel good. Pressure is stimulating, exhilarating. Pain indicates something is wrong. If pain arises, revert to an easier posture or abstain until sufficient strength is developed.

The breathing, visualization and self-massage make my yoga distinct. I encourage you to read the introductory pages to the yoga classes to familiarize you with my approach. Each class begins with a breathing/healing intro which is marked with small roman numerals (i, ii, etc). These intros are interchangeable within classes, or you can practice them alone.

In yoga class, I respond to people's energy in much the same way I do at a concert, adapting and molding the experience to the needs of those present. The classes presented here are transcribed from my morning yoga classes in Manhattan Beach, CA where I have taught for the past ten years. Wherever possible, I use Sanskrit names for clarity. Poses I have made up have made-up names. I joke around a lot in class - the laughter is my solace from a spiritual intensity I was born with. I hope you enjoy practicing yoga with me.

The second section (SELF-EXAMINATION) can be done in an hour or so when you have time and cause for reflection. The third section (CHANTING) is meant to be read, browsed and experimented with. The information is a combination of teacher training lectures and magazine articles. Interspersed throughout are transcriptions of my *dharma* talks in between songs at the concerts. These pages reflect the many ways you have asked me to come forward and I thank you for asking.

Before you begin, I want to introduce some concepts which are integral to this practice. These are the underlying foundation and philosophy for using the postures (*asana*) as a healing practice.

before you begin

energy flows

During the course of the day, your energy goes out in various activities; during yoga class, you will need to withdraw yourself into a quiet space so you can heal. The first step is *pratyahar*, or withdrawal of the senses. Closing the eyes, resting the ears by sitting in silence, closing the mouth and sitting quietly moves your body and mind from the outside world to an inner world.

I use energy seals to enhance this process. Energy seals include hand postures *(mudras)* and body positions. Sitting on your heel with your heel at the perineum seals off the first *chakra*. Interlacing your fingers above your head seals off the crown *chakra*. Pressing your first fingertip and thumbtip together in *gyan mudra* seals the energy of the hands, where energy normally escapes in the flow of *vyana*. Sealing the extremities forces the energy to recirculate. It traps the energy inside the body and makes the healing more potent.

The next step is a process of drawing energy in the opposite direction from its natural flow. Using *bandhas* (see p. 23) and visualizations, you will draw the energy in its opposite direction for a short amount of time to initiate healing. Yogic texts describe five energy flows *(vayus)* coursing through the body – *prana, apana, samana, udana* and *vyana. Prana* is forward moving energy, centered around the heart, lungs and esophagus. *Apana* is the downward moving energy, focused in the area between the navel and anus. *Samana* moves side to side, focused at the navel point. *Udana* is upward moving air, moving from the throat to the top of the head. And *vyana* is the pervasive air, moving in spirals throughout the body – from the hips to the toes, from the shoulders to the fingertips, from the throat to the top of the head. Spirals or rings of light extend outwards to the extremities.

For example, because the energy of *apana* is downward, you draw the belly towards the spine while pulling anus and perineum towards each other *(moolbandha)* to draw the lower energy up. Then, after pulling the energy up for a few minutes, you relax and watch as the energy flows with gusto, this time in the right direction. In these yoga classes, you will tense the body and then relax it. You will hold your breath in or out and then relax. You will pull the energy in, and then watch it dance inside you. Opposites enhance each other.

Many energetic patterns you hold are imprinted in childhood or learned through experience. The body you have is the standard model issued by your particular family genes. You imprinted your parent's body postures and breathing patterns by the time you were three years old. Embedded in the musculature are certain attitudes and outlooks, also subconsciously imprinted. Past life lessons and experiences are also stored energetically in the body and manifest in the physical body as well.

All *karmas* process through the physical body. Some experiences don't digest easily. Intervention and encouragement are necessary to release the effect of these *karmas* from the physical body. Energy stagnates when experiences go undigested and unprocessed, sometimes even solidifying into tumors, cysts and diseases. This is an ever-changing Universe, and energy must come and go freely through mind, body, and spirit.

the 5 vayus

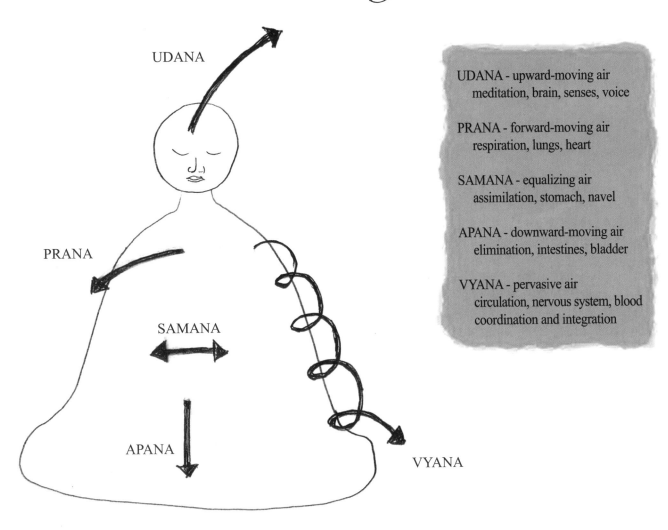

UDANA

PRANA

SAMANA

APANA

VYANA

UDANA - upward-moving air
meditation, brain, senses, voice

PRANA - forward-moving air
respiration, lungs, heart

SAMANA - equalizing air
assimilation, stomach, navel

APANA - downward-moving air
elimination, intestines, bladder

VYANA - pervasive air
circulation, nervous system, blood
coordination and integration

The practice in yoga, then, is to strengthen the normal flow of these *vayus* and then reverse them for a short time. The forward flow of *prana* is pulled inwards. The downward flow of *apana* is pulled upwards. The upward flow of *udana* is drawn in through the top of the head. The rapid side-to-side movement of *samana* at the navel point is focused at a single point. And the outward spiraling energy of *vyana* is drawn into the body spiralling inwards towards the core. When the reversal of these *vayus* is successful, the five energy flows rebound with renewed vigor and the body heals. There are some who claim this reversal of *vayus* concentrates the energy at the solar plexus, which initiates healing, change, and yogic powers.

The limitless presence of Love is what heals and guides us. But we don't always feel connected to it. We are distracted by work, family, responsibilities, relationships, holidays – in fact, any aspect of our life can prevent us from feeling connected. What prevents us from feeling connected to the beauty, love, and vigor of life is a blockage of energy flow. Physically, it can manifest as an injury. In chanting or meditation, it manifests as a recurring thought. In life, it appears as a repeating scenario. It is the lesson that repeats over and over again, waiting for resolution.

How can we realign the mind, body and spirit? The modern way is by getting new information – getting a life coach, a therapist, or a physical therapist to show you how to reorganize yourself. But the old-fashioned yogic way works just as well. It involves recycling energy.

Perhaps you have seen Tibetan prayer wheels in various temples. Large cylindrical tubes stand in a line, each one with a prayer carved into it. Handles on the bottom allow people to turn the wheels as they pass by. When the wheels turn, the prayers that are written on them are spoken by the wind. *Om Mani Padme Hum*, May All Beings Live in Peace, and other universal healing thoughts are initiated by the spinning wheels.

Mantras recycle just like the prayer wheels. No other words are spoken. The prayer keeps rotating and cycles back in on itself. In the same way, the tongue cycles in the mouth. You cannot distract yourself with idle conversation, the *mantra* cycles over and over. The energy leads you into the void. The void is where the healing happens.

As you chant a *mantra*, the process becomes your journey. You discover everything that keeps you from surrendering into the void. Small irritations of the mind are recycled back into the mind for purification. You might look at the present, at something that happened today, last week or many years ago. These thoughts are re-ingested into the system. This cycling process continues until the thoughts dissolve; they no longer surface as an issue or a blockage, on your way to the void. Eventually you get to the void and bask there.

Do you understand how much stuff comes up when you hold a posture and recycle your energy? As the *mantra* starts and you close your eyes, you may be surprised by what's there. If you could move, you might move away from those thoughts. But you can't, so the thoughts recycle and you examine them. You breathe. You watch. You breathe. You chant. Recycing is a predominant theme in yogic practices, not just in *japa* (*mantra* chanting) and *asana* (posture), but in *kumbhaka* (breath retention), *bandha* (energy lock), *mouna* (practice of silence), and *shatkarma* (physical purification of the body).

The things that block us from being in the void are our physical, emotional, and karmic patterns. You don't think you're blocked; but then an injury or life experience shows your weakness. It doesn't hold up under pressure. It's probably something that was weak in the first place, something that you needed to work on, some hidden agenda that you weren't noticing. We often cover up our weaknesses, we over-compensate with other muscles and behavior patterns; but the issue resurfaces. The blockage hurts. It keeps us from experiencing the cosmos. So you take a moment from your busy life and pause. You look at it. You work on it. You recycle your energies and become still. In the precious void, healing and reintegration begins.

visualization

There is a sanskrit word for inner awareness: *yoga nidra*. *Nidra* means sleep and *yoga* means inner communion. Often introduced during *savasana* at the end of class, *yoga nidra* uses guided imagery to create healing effects in body, mind and spirit. I find it extends into asana practice, meditation and even everyday activities. I invite you to start a practice of visualization the moment you begin your yoga. If it feels tight or constricted, breathe into that area. If you have a sore shoulder, send healing light to your shoulder. If your kidneys won't expand when you breathe (they really do widen on the inhale), send spacious healing light to your kidneys. Visualize how you want your body to be: full of light.

I am doing this practice constantly throughout class. If the energy won't respond to visualization and breathing, I resort to body beating, massage and body drops. I respond to what I see and feel. You should develop a conversation within your body. If an area looks gray, the energy is stagnant. If you find a place where energy is blocked, send a suggestion to heal. Don't command it to heal, ask gently for light and love to fill that area and resolve any emotions surrounding the blockage. Yawn, cry, laugh, do whatever feels good to release the energy. Be thankful for the opportunity to be alone with yourself and heal. Send messages of encouragement into your system; your body responds to kindness & enthusiasm.

The Mind Screen is a platform for visualization. If you close your eyes and look into your eyelids, you will see a blank screen. Relax the eyes, don't look for anything; it's more like sleeping, dreaming, or gazing. Open the eyes and retain the feeling of the mind screen. Your gaze will soften as you experience inner and outer vision together. Now, close your eyes again and direct the eyes upwards towards the 3rd eye. Place a blue flame there. You can meditate like this for many hours. Now keep the eyes turning upwards but relaxed. This reveals a wider screen. The eyes can wander slightly even while the eyes turn up into the head. This is called "the sky of the mind" or you may hear me say, "In your mind's eye, see the body covered in light..." Using the mind screen, you can create an image of your body. It doesn't have to be accurate. You can see structure or energy patterns of physical body parts. Some people see geometric energy structures, others see pulsating colors. It doesn't matter how it appears to you; accept what you see as your way of communicating between mind, body and spirit. If this seems too advanced, watch your breath enter and exit your body, noticing where the energy comes in and how it moves. This is a good starting point for self-healing and visualization. Through the practice of *yoga nidra* in *savasana*, you will gain familiarity with the body parts, functions and energies and your visualization skills will improve.

I add imagery to the breath, using both inhale and exhale as vehicles for healing. For beginners, visualize new energy coming in on the inhale, and old energy going out on the exhale. Inhale what you need in your life and exhale what you need to release. Inhale light, exhale patterns which no longer serve you. Inhale the present moment, exhale yesterday's interactions. And so on. For more advanced students, a nonlinear approach is suitable, attracting positive aspects on the inhale and integrating them into the *chakras* on the exhale. This approach takes on a different energy pattern - instead of expelling unwanted qualities, the good energy is stored and increased until it expands in a radiating pattern from the core, naturally dominating the system with positive aspects.

Tell me, what are you going to bring in on the breath today? You can attract whatever you need from the Universe, just bring it in. Pick something, make it your commodity. Get in the business and start buying and selling it. What did you pick? Love. You want love? Draw that energy into your body through the breath. Buy and sell love. Breathe it. Be it. Put it on the breath. Make it your intention. Need money? Wisdom? Peace of mind? Whatever it is, place it on the breath. Inhale joy, light, wisdom, or any positive quality you would like to attract.

body purification

Layers of conditioning, trauma and stress block free energy flow in the body. Body purifications heal and purge the body of unwanted stagnant thoughts and energy patterns. Your energetic work is initiated by unblocking your physical passageways.

Simple foods and an uncomplicated lifestyle will support a healthy body and mind. I recommend a simple diet of fresh, unprocessed foods and lots of fresh air. Keep it fun. Instead of *neti*, you can go surfing and get a noseful of salt water as you tumble in the waves. Hot tubs of hydrogen peroxide, salt water swimming pools, even chlorine pools can purify. Fresh air is the best - walk outdoors in the woods or along the ocean and absorb nature's *prana*.

Receiving healing treatments is so beneficial; there are wonderful healers out there - reiki, acupuncture, thai massage, ayurvedic massage, network chiropractic and chiropractic are some of my favorites. The information your body provides to your healer might also give you insight and increased awareness about your life patterns.

Don't limit yourself to just the body. Clean your surroundings, your home, your altar, your yoga room, your community. Cleaning the environment around you will also clear your mind. Clean out your closets, give away what you don't use, keep the energy in your life moving. What is inside is reflected outside. Make the outside temple beautiful. Inside will follow.

Beauty. Be clean, both yourself and the place you live in, Understand and respect your body. It is the temple of the spirit.
                    -Native American, Laws of Woodcraft

Yogic texts describe six shatkarmas or cleansing practices for the body. Daily clearing of the tongue, intestines, stomach, sinuses, lungs, and skin is recommended.

tongue, teeth, gums *(dhauti) Take two fingers and rub them along the back part of your tongue to create a slight retching action. Cough out the phlegm which has collected in the throat. If your eyes water, you're doing it right; tears remove stagnant fluid from the eyes. Then take those same two fingers and rub your gums to stimulate blood flow and flush away stagnant energy in the teeth and gums. Wash your hands thoroughly after you are finished.*

sinus *(neti) Pour salt water in one nostril and let it flow out the other. There are neti pots you can buy for this purpose. An alternative is snuffing salt water in the nose from a cupped hand and spitting it out your mouth (vyutkrama) but it is not as effective as neti.*

intestine *(basti) When impure food or improper lifestyle have polluted the system, an old-fashioned enema cleanses the intestinal walls.*

stomach *(nauli) Exhale your breath out and hold. Suck the stomach in towards the spine and release it 5-7 times. Inhale relax. Repeat.*

eyes *(trataka) Gaze unblinkingly at a candle, mandala or meditation picture. Or cup the palms over the eyes and gaze into the mind's eye.*

brain *(kapalbhati) Breathing practices and scalp massage can awaken the brain.*

Rub the palms together, bringing the fingertips to the insides of the wrists. Gather healing energy between the hands. Place the hands over the eyes, sealing out any light, and gaze two miles into the distance at the level of the horizon. Hold the eyes unblinkingly open. Relax the sides and back of the head.

Neuro-linguistic research has found upwards eye movement corresponds to visual information, side to side eye movement to auditory information and downwards eye movement to kinesthetic information. Go ahead, try and remember your last vacation, you will look up as you recall visual memories. Fun, isn't it? Just know that your eyes and thought patterns are intricately linked. By holding the eyes steady, your thought process slows. Gazing instead of looking relaxes the eyes. When your eyes relax, your mind and psyche expand. In yoga, gazing is called

trataka which awakens and stimulates the pituitary and pineal glands, master glands of the sympathetic nervous system. Don't look for things. Just see what's in front of you. Rather than squinting or searching for things, practice gazing and let things come. At first, you will not be able to hold your eyes steady or keep your eyes unblinkingly open. Don't worry. With practice your eyes will relax.

Bring the hands together at the center of the chest. Press your fingertips and thumbtips together in front of the heart, drawing the shoulder blades together along the back. Create a wholeness at the heart by drawing the energy together in front (pressing fingertips together) and in back (drawing shoulder blades together). Then press the mounds of the fingers together, and then palms. Press equally with both hands. Bring light into the body on the inhale and chant *Om*. Hear the sound inside you and outside you. Listen to the sound as you create it. Vibrate with the sound. Chant *Om* two more times. Inhale, hold for a moment and then exhale and let the healing energy settle.

open your heart
not to me but to everything
your world, your eyes
your love, your lies
everything

open your heart
not a moment but all the time
until the colors of all life
are part of you inside

pranayama

I am amazed at how different I feel after yoga class. I thought I was okay. I thought I was breathing well. After breathing practices *(pranayama)*, I wonder how I even made it to yoga class. *Pranayama* initiates the healing process in your yoga practice.

Try to balance what goes in and out of your body. Take in and give away. Give away the same amount you take in. It's hard isn't it? We take some in and take some more. We hold onto things - possessions, experiences, emotions - and they just sit there. Or maybe you're the one who gives and gives until you are depleted, ignoring your own needs and pushing beyond your limits. Balancing the breath is one way to train the mind to balance incoming and outgoing energy.

Broken breaths 4 part breathing Break the breath into 4 equal parts. Be aware of your breathing process and try to do each step fully. To start, inhale 4 equal sniffs and exhale 4 equal sniffs. I will talk you through it: Inhale a little bit, inhale a little more, inhale puff the rib cage in all directions, inhale all the way, and hold one, hold two, hold three, hold four. Now exhale just a little bit, exhale a little more and watch your rib cage come to a relaxed position (I call this neutral), exhale more, press the air out and keep the heart high, press all the air out, and hold one, hold two, hold three, hold four. Each of the four counts lasts the same duration, so the rhythm remains constant.

You can mentally honor the four directions as you hold the breath, attach a mantra, or simply count to four. If you want to expand the inhale, you might envision smelling a rose or your favorite food. To enhance the exhale, you might voluntarily cough or shudder. These are good signs. To expand your breath capacity you will need to exaggerate each side of the breathing process, both inhale and exhale.

When you divide the breath into 4 equal parts, breath two is neutral. Inhale, inhale (this is neutral), inhale more and expand, inhale as much as you can and expand all the way, hold, hold, hold, hold, exhale, exhale again (this is neutral), exhale and press the air out, exhale and press all the air out. What is neutral? Neutral is how your rib cage naturally sits when you are relaxed. If you put your hands on your rib cage right now you will feel the rib cage at neutral. During inhalation, the ribs expand to the sides (into your hands) and to the back (into your thumbs), bottom (the diaphragm pushes down on the stomach and other organs) and top (under the collarbones). During exhalation, the ribs relax back to neutral first, and then deflate towards each other as the exhalation completes. The heart remains at the same level throughout the breathing process. The heart is like a lotus floating in the water. Don't let the heart sink when you exhale.

If your lungs were like a balloon, your inhale would fill the balloon. The beginning of the exhale would return the balloon to its natural form, and the end of the exhale would suck the air out it. Beginning of the inhale would return the balloon to its natural form and the end of the inhale would puff it up. This means breaths #1 and #2 are controlled relaxation; the rib cage wants to return to neutral. Breaths #3 and #4 are where the real work happens, either expanding the lungs (inhalation) or pressing the air out (exhalation).

After a few minutes of 4-part breathing, you can inhale and **hold the breath** for 20 seconds. Puff the body in all directions. You may feel a pushing action as you seal off the windpipe and expand. Now exhale, inhale, and exhale all the air out. Seal off the windpipe and hold for 20 seconds. Notice the suction as you hold the breath out. You can see this suction at the neck as the collarbones become exposed. You can create this suction with or without a full exhalation - simply seal off the windpipe and attempt to breathe in. When you relax the windpipe, you will hear a sound as the air comes rushing back in. Work up to 30 seconds of breath retention at the end of your pranayama sequence. With practice, you will be able to retain your breath 40-60 seconds.

Breath retention *(kumbukha)* is a great tool and is often combined with **energy locks** *(bandhas)*. There are three main *bandhas*. Root lock *(mool bandh)* seals off the bottom of the spine by contracting the perineum and anus towards each other for men, or squeezing the vaginal opening and anus towards each other for women. Diaphragm lock *(uddiyana bandh)* pulls the energy from the navel up to the heart by pulling the diaphragm up into the body cavity. Neck lock *(jalandar bandh)* pulls the energy from the throat up to the top of the head, by tucking the chin in and/or moving the upper palete back.

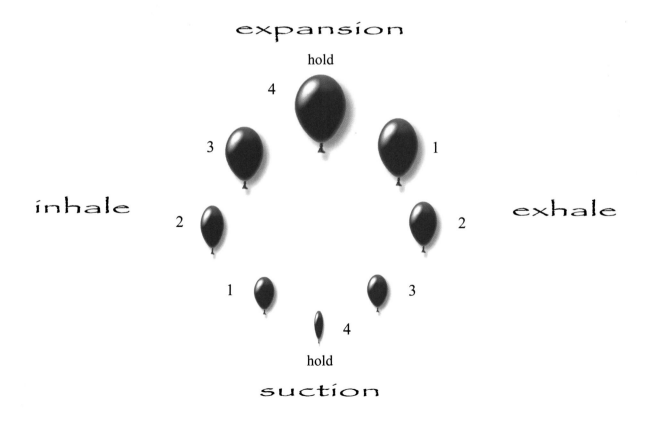

The first step in yogic breathing is balancing inhale and exhale. These exercises focus on balancing the breath and developing the diaphragm muscle:

Alternate nostril breathing - With your right thumb block off your right nostril and inhale through your left nostril. Using your middle or ring finger, block off the left nostril and exhale through the right. Extend your left arm out to the side, palm facing heaven, stretching the thumb to the floor behind you and keeping the palm flat. To do the other side, reverse the arms and inhale: right nostril, exhale: left nostril.

Bellows breathing *(bhastrika pranayama)* is one sniff in and one sniff out. Lie down on your back, interlace your fingers behind your neck underneath any hair and bring your palms flat against the sides of your neck to create a sealed connection. Join your heels together to seal the energy at the bottom of the body, and begin *bhastrika pranayama* through the nose, inhaling and exhaling equal amounts. Don't force the diaphragm, allow the breath to come and go easily. Inhale and exhale equal amounts.

Broken breaths 8 part breathing - inhale 8 parts, exhale 8 parts - sitting in a comfortable position, join the first finger and thumb in *gyan mudra* and bring the hands touching the ground beside you, palms facing earth. Keeping the arms straight, raise the arms overhead in 8 equal movements as you inhale in 8 parts, and lower the arms in 8 equal movements as you exhale in 8 parts. Continue for several minutes and then inhale raise the arms, exhale and relax.

inhalation

The second step in yogic breathing is extending the duration of the breath, making it longer and slower. This is enhanced by constricting the air passageway. These exercises extend the inhalation:

Whisper breathing *(ujjayi pranayama)* - Closing off the back of the throat as if you were whispering, breathe through the nose slowly and methodically. *Ujjayi* breathing is done exclusively through the nose but the constriction of the throat limits the flow of air. It sounds a little like Darth Vader from *Star Wars*.

Curled tongue *(seetali pranayama)* - Curl tongue lengthwise so it protrudes from lips, inhale slowly over tongue, exhale through nose.

Puckered lips - For those who can't curl their tongue (it's hereditary, don't take it personally), pucker the lips and inhale through puckered lips, exhale through nose. If you make a tight circle with the lips, you will feel like you are sucking the air in through a straw; this is good. The inhalation should be long and slow. If the lips are too loose, the air will come in too fast and your inhalation will not be any longer than a normal breath.

Whistle - Even more fun than puckered lips breathing! Inhale through puckered lips on a whistle, exhale through the nose. This creates an other-worldly sound as well as increasing the length of the inhale.

Crow's breath *(kaki pranayama)* (practice on an empty stomach) - Inhale through puckered lips and "chew" the air as you hold it in, inhale puckered lips, chew the air, etc. At maximum inhalation, retain breath and churn the ribcage (see p.32) in a clockwise direction, come center and exhale. Practice 3 or 4 times only.

Yawn - Yawning is the body's natural way of releasing tension and bringing extra oxygen to specific muscles or organs. Yawning is an exaggerated inhalation. If you have the desire to yawn in a certain posture, go back to that exact position and allow the yawn to unfold. I occasionally include yawning as an exercise in a group class.

exhalation

It is easier to extend the length of the exhalation than it is to extend the inhalation. These exercises extend the length of exhalation:

Whisper breathing *(ujjayi pranayama)* - Closing off the back of the throat as if you were whispering, breathe through the nose slowly and methodically. *Ujjayi* breathing naturally slows down the pace of the breath, allowing you to extend the duration of both inhale and exhale. If you've never tried it before, open the mouth and whisper, keep whispering and close the mouth. It's kind of a Ha-ummmm on a whisper. It is easier for most people to create the distinctive *ujjayi* whisper sound on the exhalation so I usually teach it on the exhalation first.

Bumble bee breath *(bhramari pranayama)* - Well, you might call it motor boat, and kids call it race car driving, but the yogis call it bumble bee. Inhale through the nose and exhale through pursed lips. The lips will vibrate as the sound escapes. If your lips won't vibrate, pucker your lips out a bit and then press them harder together as you exhale through the mouth. Singers use this technique to determine if enough support is being given from the diaphragm. If the diaphragm is not engaged, the lips won't bubble. This exercise increases the length of the exhale, engages the diaphragm and brings blood and energy to the face.

Hiss - Lying on the back or sitting upright, inhale through the nose, exhale and place the tongue near the front teeth to exhale on a hiss. Hissing extends the length of the exhale and engages the diaphragm.

Whistle - In any posture, exhale on a whistle through puckered lips. This extends the length of the exhale and does something to the inner ear with its other-worldly sound. Many whistlers in one room, even if they whistle on different tones, will create a spacey, meditative atmosphere.

Sing - Singing also increases the duration of the exhale and engages the diaphragm. I use singing playfully, asking students to sing "Morning has Broken" by Cat Stevens or some song that everyone knows. Singing or chanting in a posture extends the length of the exhale.

Laughter - Open the mouth and let the air escape forcefully as you say 'ha!' and again 'ha!' It will eventually lead to spontaneous laughter, which you can embellish with any vowel sounds you want (hee hee, ha ha, ho ho). Laughter is generated at the belly and is an amazing workout for the diaphragm.

Open mouth whisper – Lying on the back, inhale through the nose, exhale through an open mouth whisper. This is a slow breath, allowing release of toxins. In the movie *Green Mile*, the healer expels ash from his mouth after healing someone. You can do the same. Exhale slowly and visualize ash flying out of your mouth, releasing unwanted impurities and old energies.

Open mouth sigh – Lying on the back, inhale through the nose, exhale and sigh through the mouth. When you lie on back, only the inhale requires effort. Exhale is a complete letting go. Sitting or standing, both inhale and exhale require effort; but lying down, you can relax on the exhale. Open mouth sigh is good lying on the back, in downward dog or other resting postures. I prefer a slight whisper sound in the throat so the sigh doesn't escape too quickly.

Lion's breath *(simhasana)* - Inhale through the nose, exhale and open your mouth, extending the tip of the tongue to your chin. You can widen the eyes or go cross-eyed. Claw the fingers into the ground. It's a scary face, so go for it. This exercise releases toxins from the body, you may taste them on your tongue. Traditionally, this exercise is practiced sitting on the heels, hands on the floor in front of you, but can also be practiced in cow pose or other postures.

Lastly, I share with you agnisara, or diaphragm pumps which increase the strength and capacity of the diaphragm, one of the main muscles used in the breathing process. Also known as agni kriya.

Fire purification *(agnisara dhauti)* **-** Come sitting on the heels, toes tucked under, hands on the thighs, rise up off the heels and look down at the navel point. I lovingly call this *vomit asana* because this is a common posture for helping *apana* or getting rid of unwanted impurities from the body. Inhale deeply, then exhale and hold the breath out while pulling the navel back towards the spine. If you are familiar with diaphragm lock (*uddiyana bandh)*, suck the diaphragm up in toward the heart. Whichever you choose, pull it and relax the stomach, pull and relax 3-7 times and then inhale. Do this 4 times.

Agnisara increases the digestive juices, the fire of digestion, and develops the strength of the diaphragm muscle. Although the Gerhand Samhita describes the possibility of 108 pumps per exhalation, I believe 3-7 pumps per exhalation is enough for daily practice. Try to relax the stomach entirely in between pumps, allowing the stomach to hang loose. Yes, it's ugly. Don't let that deter you.

inside of **wrists to temples** - make small circles.

grab ears – pull up, pull down, pull back, squeeze along outer rim of ear from top to earlobe.

inside of **wrists to ears** - rub up and down vigorously.

scalp massage - press fingertips and thumbtips into scalp, or grab tufts of hair and gently pull hair back and forth to move scalp over skullbone.

back of head massage - lying on back, roll head on ground, bringing chin to right shoulder, chin to left shoulder.

massage

these massage techniques stimulate energy release

neck massage - with your L hand reach behind neck and place fingers on one side, heel of hand on the other side of the spine. Squeeze the fingers and heel of hand together, massaging the neck vertebrae and shoulder (trapezius).

lymph massage - L fingertips move in circular pattern, massaging chest, front of shoulder, underarm, and rib cage. Switch (R hand massages L side).

larynx massage - two fingers on either side of larynx, move side to side.

intestinal massage - hands on waist, dig fingers in front, thumbs in back, squeeze thumbs and fingers together to massage intestines, alternating R and L.

forehead massage - from baby pose *(balasana)*, rest elbows on floor, roll forehead side to side on the floor.

shudder - seated or lying down, shudder the body making an 'S' with the spine.

navel pulse - sit on the heels, gather the fingertips and thumbtip of the right hand together into a single point and place in the bellybutton. With the left hand press the right hand into the navel and lean forward placing the forehead on the ground. You will feel the navel pulse beating under your fingers. You may have to move your hand a little to the left or right to find the exact location of the navel pulse. Breathe deeply; it's intense. This can also be done lying on the back.

inchworm - on stomach, raise hips and drop them down to the floor.

wag ankles and wrists - lying on back or stomach.

windshield wipers on back – soles of feet by buttocks feet 24" apart, drop both knees to R then L.

windshield wipers on stomach - bend knees, wag ankles side to side, or apart & together.

egg beaters - same as windshield wipers but feet make large circles. Can be practiced on stomach (pictured here) or on back with legs raised to sky.

these exercises release tension at the sacrum and head, two common target areas for clenching and stress.

release

inhale and fill the belly with air/ exhale and completely let go - lying on stomach, the belly presses against the earth as it expands, then releases. Lying on back, belly expands to sky on inhale, releases down on exhale.

relax the eyes - let your eyes rest in your head, relaxing all muscles around the eyes.

unclench your jaw (lips are touching, teeth are not touching).

in baby pose, **dump your problems** into the earth through 3rd eye.

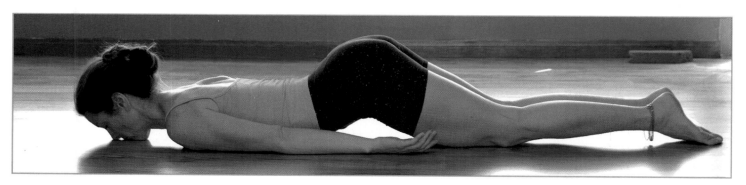

falling in love

These paths lead to Love. Any path. Not a spiritual one, not an artistic one, not a serviceful one. Every life journey leads to Love. In the end, this will be your conclusion. Love. Love for yourself. Love for the people in and around your life, who are also working towards selflessness. Love. It's the end all. If you have reached any other conclusion, you're not finished yet. Love will be your last thought after you've worked it all out. It's not a concept. It's a feeling that permeates everything you do. Love is rushing at you, every minute of the day.

Love. If you've tasted it once, you want to taste it again. An artist will remember being at one with a creative energy and having the painting flow into completion. He or she will want to experience that again. A meditator will remember the experience of deep absorption, and will strive to reproduce it.

You know what love is. You had a grandparent or a teacher or a sibling or a lover who showed you love. You will never forget that feeling. They cared for you. Gave you special attention. You meant something. Can you remember someone who cared for you like that? The way that person loved you is exactly the same way the whole Universe co-exists with you. The energy of Love that you receive is special and personal. It has enormous impact. Through your relationship with the Universe, you understand that your being is special. You realize that what you have to offer in this life is vital and means so much. Each human life is taken very seriously in the spirit realm, did you know that? What you do with each life and each situation is enormously important. What you are doing right now is the result of many efforts before this. You have tried before to get to this point. And here you are – hoping to be able to let go and open to a higher energy. And you're dragged down with this person or that situation, and wondering how can it all work out? How can you *ever* get to a place of self-acceptance, a feeling of oneness... Constant loving care creates the change.

You fall in love with certain things, on your way to falling in love with everything. You worship certain people, certain idols, certain beings, on your way to worshipping all that is. It starts with a personal connection, someone who shows special interest in you or shares a special connection. Universal love comes later. I invite you to make your practice personal.

Things you love are given space in your life because they connect you to what you need. That's why you travel hundreds of miles to see your loved one. Or to be with a saint. Or to go to a concert. You want to feel open, expansive, free. You want to feel that space of selflessness within yourself.

What will you find in your practice? You will find your self, whatever that is. Whatever is in you will surface. If you can approach yourself with love and kindness, you will enjoy and delight in what you find. You can't use your eyes to decipher this stuff. You must learn with your heart. Let your desires lead you. In meditative life, personal desires and soul desires become the same thing. Trust your deepest feelings.

Use your heart and soul to seek out the energies that feed you. Listen to your heart's desires. What are you longing for? Observe what is and then pray for what you want it to be. Seek out experiences of bliss. Create joyful activities to adorn your day. Bliss is available at every moment. Hafiz, Rumi, Ramakrishna – their lives were directed by an inner thirst, a passion for the sacredness of every moment. You must have this thirst also because you are reading this book.

Come, let's explore an inner world of healing and self-discovery, and fall into love....

class 1

(i) 4 part breathing - Inhale 4 parts, hold 4 parts, exhale 4 parts, hold 4 parts. (see p. 22)

(ii) churning the rib cage – Sitting in easy pose, hold onto your knees and move rib cage in a circle, pressing hands into the knees to increase the twist of your rib cage. 1 1/2 minutes each direction.

(ii)

1

paschima=back or west
uttan=stretch
If you start your practice facing east, your back will face west.

1 forward stretch sitting on one heel (*paschimottanasana*) - Sit on your right heel and stretch your left leg out in front of you, hands by hips, inhale up, exhale hinge forward bringing the rib cage to the thighs. 2 min.

The first *chakra* starts at the perineum for men and at the cervix for women. Sealing the energy at the first chakra allows the energy in the body to collect and increase. So, place the heel at the perineum. If you have trouble doing that, lift the hips off the ground, tip the hips forward and then sit down on the heel.

2 cat and cow (*bidalasana* and *marjaryasana*) - Inhale and bring the navel towards the earth, exhale and bring the navel towards heaven. 2 min.

3 wrist strengthening on all 4s - Placing hands on ground under the shoulders, spread your fingers like the rays of the sun, lift heels of hands off the ground and relax them down. Bring the weight of hands between the first two fingers so the hands don't sickle. The more weight you put on your hands, the more strengthening you develop in wrists and palms.

4 cat cow & wrist strengthening at the same time - Move spine and practice wrist strengthening, squeezing your forearms towards midline. Like a plant, use the root like structure of the fingers to draw nourishment from the earth, pulling the energy into your heart. You can lift feet off ground and circle ankles as well for some added fun! 1 min.

5 sitting camel - With hands interlaced behind you, shrug shoulders up, drop head back, *bhastrika pranayama* for 1 minute, then inhale and bring the rib cage forward to the thighs and let the chin slowly return to normal, lengthen the spine. Rest and repeat another round or two.

6 pranam to prone - Sitting on the heels, bring the forehead to the floor and stretch the arms overhead. Leaving the hands where they are, come up onto all 4s and bring the heart and head down to the ground at the same time. Lift the shoulders away from the ground first, then inhale and squeeze the hands towards each other and the knees towards each other as you come up to all 4s. Exhale as you sit back on the heels and bring your forehead to the ground. Inhale as you go, exhale when you get there. 1 min.

7 one leg bow *(ek pada dhanurasana)* - Lying on stomach, bend R leg and grab ankle with R hand. If you are more flexible, you can grab ankle with both hands, interlacing fingers around ankle. Breathe long and deep for 1 minute, then rest. Switch sides. For added fun, rock forward and back on the stomach.

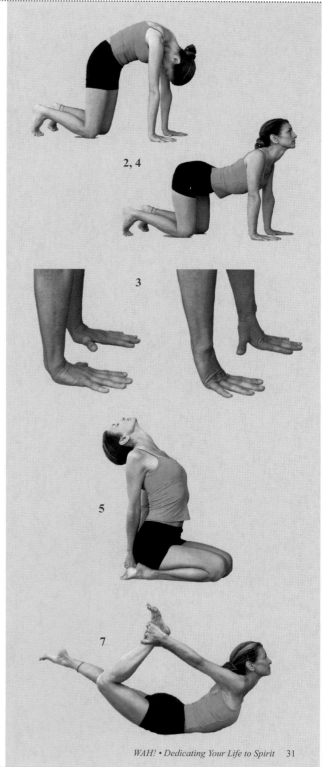

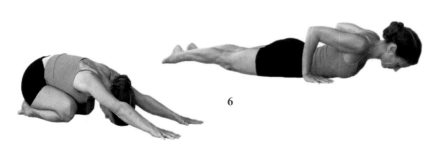

class 1

10

8 inchworm on stomach - Raise hips off the floor and then drop them down. For more challenge, you can alternately lift hips and heart, inching forward and back on your mat. 1 min.

9 body shudder - Lying on stomach, make a quick S movement in the spine, then relax. Do this 3 or 4 times. Heart and head move in opposite directions.

10 two leg raise - Lying on back, inhale and raise arms overhead, raise legs to 90°, exhale lower legs, lower arms to the floor. 30 times.

11 alternate head and leg raise - Lying on back, keep arms on ground overhead, inhale raise feet 6" off ground, exhale lower legs and raise head to look at feet. 20 times

11

Cultivate purity, maintain a regular schedule of eating and exercise, hold some things precious in your life, withdraw regularly from the world, breathe until your mind has no weight, absorb yourself in silence often. Cultivate total enthusiasm for your life work and be at peace with each step along the way.

12 fish pose (*matseyasana*) - With your legs straight out in front of you, hands by the hips fingers facing forward, lean back on your forearms and pull the heart up towards heaven. Breathe deeply. 1 min.

13 rolling bug - Bring your knees to your chest and roll to the R into a fetal position. Roll to center and then to the L, rolling head on the floor. If you move your arms first, before your legs, you can enjoy spinal twist. 2 min.

14 bridge (*setubandhasana*) - Lying on your back, bring your heels to the buttocks, palms facing earth or fingers wrapped around the outside of the heel, thumbs on the inside of the heel. Inner spiral the legs, lift the hips up, draw the shoulder blades together and breathe. Lower down and relax. Continue for 1 1/2 min.

15 backbends - From bridge pose, place your hands on either side of your head, bringing the top of your head on the floor, melt the heart by drawing the shoulder blades together along the back. Lift the heart and come into backbend. Do 3 or 4 backbends, relaxing in corpse pose in between backbends.

16 savasana

12

13

14

15

16

heart open ···· eyes closed

Your eyes engage your brain. When your eyes are open, you see things, calculate which way to go, who that is, what your relationship with them is... With your eyes closed it's less clear. It ceases to be logical. Your thoughts come and go. Your brain is engaged in an inner world.

Your practice begins with a moment of softness, a moment of spaciousness. It's as simple as putting a flower in the corner of your house. It's some small acknowledgment, some small reminder you create in the world, that reminds you the hand of God is present. Placing a small flower on the statue by the door on your way out, or on the doorstep, something like that. It's a softening. You see yourself in a larger picture, you see yourself in god's hand. And then who knows? In India, they often turn their head side to side. You'll get that response for "yes" and that same response for "no". "Is it this way?" you ask. Response (turning head this way and that), "Could be." My son was in India asking for thirds on dahl, which is almost an impossibility in India. But he's tall (6'2") and he wanted more dahl, so he went to ask for more. There was nothing in the serving container. The man did not say, "There's no more." No, he said, "Let me check in the kitchen." Now, there's no more in the kitchen, he knows that. But he doesn't say no. He doesn't finalize it. Instead he says, "Just five minutes." Because, who knows? Things could change in five minutes. Some food could arrive from somewhere, something could happen. *Shiva* could manifest some food on the stove. Could be.

Sometimes it seems that everything in India appears to be coming in "just five minutes." But do you see how that mental framework leaves you open? As Americans, we tend to say, "Can't you see there's no more rice?! It's gone. It's plain to see." And so we nod our heads yes or no, because we see. In our world, we see that something is either present or absent. But once you close your eyes, things change. The lines start to blur.

My practice brings me to a halfway energy, a place in between the boundaries of what I say is reality and what is mystical or magical. I am here in an incarnation experiencing something that I think is real, but when I close my eyes down I have a different experience of it. If I can float into a higher frequency, rotate a little bit faster, I can see the world differently. For me, I can only get there if I soften. I have to soften to acknowledge this is the hand of God. And then, what happens is a result of this opening. Anything could happen…

Next time someone asks you, "Are you successful? How's your marriage going?" just turn your head from side to side, India-style, and say, "Could be." Then the whole world remains open to you. If you say, "I am successful" you might fall on your face the next day. The moment you announce it to the Universe, it sees it as potential for fun, to prove the opposite is true, or switch things around (Let's Play a New Game). Then you're bankrupt or corrupt or whatever it is. It might be better to turn your head side to side and acknowledge "some coming, some going." It leaves all possibilities open, and leaves you open to all the possibilities.

This whole thing that is going on in the last two or three years with planetary alignments and harmonic convergence and harmonic concordance, and all of our work on ourselves, is resulting in the manifestation of more light. It might not feel like you are holding more light, but it is so. We are able to contain more energy in our bodies, our minds, our lives. We are moving towards an age where practices of light and higher frequencies are more readily available. We are moving back towards the Golden Age. And that feels different. Well, at least it feels different to me. Sometimes the first time you contain more light it feels like you are being electrocuted. Because there's more energy. You think you can't handle it. You think your brain is going to blow a fuse, that you can't take any more stuff going on in your life, but you can. It's just that you have embodied more light and it takes a little while to get used to. And as a society it takes a little while to get used to as well, that we can function with each other out of a place of light. It asks for more compassion, more understanding, more acceptance when we deal with each other. Because you don't know the whole picture; it's impossible to see all of it - softening will help you disengage from what you think you know, and see the hand of God working through you. Who knows? Really, I mean, who can comprehend what is really happening to all of us here.

I was interviewed by a radio station in Cleveland today. It was not really a conversation. The interviewer had a snippet as a lead-in. "So, you do chanting…." I think that was my cue to deliver my message; I was supposed to have something prepared. But I generally don't prepare for things, and I wasn't prepared to give her a media byte. It took us both a little off-guard. I am not like other authors and lecturers; I don't have a prepared schtick. I travel around the country trying to share no-mind with everyone. Sharing a presence, an elevated state of being. Not as a scientific how-to, but as an experience of hanging out. I explore feeling content, softening. It's playful or very serious, or whatever it is. Like I said, I am trying to make my world with eyes open closer to my world eyes-closed. I am not saying, "Do you see that *Ganesha* statue over there? That's where we're going." No. I'm saying, "We're going to close our eyes together and see what happens." For me, it's almost like I invited everyone into my meditation room. All 500 people, all crowded around my altar. We're hanging out. I appreciate ya'll coming and meditating with me. It's different than a show. When I see you twice a year or once a year, I am looking: are you closer? People see me, and say "Ahh, you look closer." Or maybe not. I see someone who looks exactly the same as he did last year, and I can say "Ah, you integrated this year." Because there were no major life changes. And someone else whose life fell apart and went through enormous changes will show an amazing amount of internal growth. You can see it in their eyes, feel it in their presence. What are we searching for? That feeling of going a little closer, embodying a little more light.

It means that all the things that are not light have to go. For me, that always feels a little squeamish. As if something hidden has suddenly been revealed to the light. That?! I squirm, Certainly not that. That doesn't have to go. My guide sits silently, waiting for me to "get it". Yes, *that* has to go too. You thought that was your own, but actually it's not a personal item at all. It's a personal framework that's hindering you from becoming who you are. No! It's *mine!* … And eventually you let it go, and you feel quite a bit freer actually. But we hold on to things. I don't even know I'm doing it. Personal dissolves into universal.

What's left after the freak-out? After you have your nervous breakdown, you are left with your connection. You thought that piece you were hanging onto was your connection, but actually it was just a sugar-coating around the connection. When it dissolves you are left with the connection and it feels very powerful. It's a "Whoa!" or "Wow!" kind of experience. Aha, you think, so this is what the connection feels like. Unfiltered. And from this experience, everything is possible. Everything. More rice, new relationships, no relationships, it's all possible from this state.

We're not going anywhere. We're not trying to achieve anything. We're just trying to soften together. As you soften, some of that polyurethane coating comes off. You haven't heard of polyurethane? It's a clear plastic coating they paint on things to protect them. We do that with our Selves. You can see the person, you can see who they are, but because of the protective coating, you can't access it. You can't feel it. It's the same with yourself. You know who you are. But you're covered with this polyurethane coating. So you can't feel it. You can't sustain it. How to get the coating off? That's what the teachers are for. If you don't have teachers, the Universe steps in and asks you to do things that you have no skills for. The agitation created by you trying to do something you think you can't do, is what burns off the polyurethane. After you are done, you are left with your connection. Ahh. And then, the next situation. More burning off, more agitation, more new skills born out of nowhere. And then, a sense of connection, peace. And so it goes.

You are asked to activate frequencies you don't have. With or without a teacher, you are asked to grow. You are asked to develop the areas which are hidden. It creates light in the being. All cells must rotate at a faster frequency. Stuff comes in faster and goes faster. It becomes like oil and water. Stay connected, and your stuff can slip off like water slides over oil. It doesn't stick; that's good. You don't want to get stuck; it slows your frequency down. It slows the rate of rotation of your *chakras*. You want your energies to rotate at a rapid rate. Things of spirit rotate rapidly. Things of earth are dense, they rotate at a slower frequency. It's simple physics applied to the energies of the psyche.

When things move faster, compassion becomes more important. If you are driving down the road at 20 miles an hour and you go off the road a little, you just correct your steering and get back on the road. But when you space out going 90 miles an hour, if you overreact, your car will be upside down in no time. As things go faster, we have to be more gentle, more kind. There must be some bugs hitting your windshield as you drive along. There are some beings harmed or killed by your actions. It's unavoidable. As you move along in your life, it's likely that you have harmed someone. Not that you wanted to, or that was your intention. But those events come to pass. The kindness has to be there. If you hurt someone along the way, offer kindness and blessing. Make amends.

You see, you will fight with some people, it's part of the process. Only New Age music and religion portray a life in the clouds, one big happy family, everything is fine, we are all one. But this is not real. The fighting is part of life. The agitation is part of what helps you grow. When the fights come, you should thank that person for helping you burn off your polyurethane. They won't understand what you're talking about, but that's OK. There is a story about a saint who sat on the bank of a river near a scorpion. The scorpion kept stinging the saint. Someone asked the saint, why don't you just move? Why do you sit there and let that scorpion sting you like that? Why don't you protect yourself and sit somewhere else. He said, we are both doing what we do. I am a saint; my nature is to bless. He is a scorpion; his nature is to sting. So he is stinging and I am blessing. We are quite comfortable here... God must think you are strong enough to take it. The process burns off what you don't need. And through it, you find your connection is stronger.

What I try and do is find someone with more voltage than me. And then I go and hang out with them. But it's not always that easy. One year when the Amma visit was over, I felt myself open in a way I had never experienced before. I knew I could not sustain it on my own. I was devastated, "How can you leave?! I can't live without this presence you have shown me, and now you are going to disappear from my life for another year." I felt so much pain, it was unbearable. It felt as if my heart was breaking. I had been shown how to live in a higher frequency, but it was only a glimpse. I couldn't create it on my own. And I knew I should die without it. What to do? I wrote "Come to Me" to remind myself of the energy. I recorded it on a cassette tape and took it back to work with me. I listened to this song and I felt like I was having a heart attack. Not just while I listened to the song, but constantly, I felt like my heart was going to rip in two. This went on for a year; doctors could not decipher if there was something wrong. I would go to work and function wonderfully and then go back to my room and listen to the tape and sob. I sang and sobbed and sang and sobbed, and a year later I was finally at a different frequency and the pain was gone. Two years later was finally able to record it. It takes longer than you think, to change the heart.

Amma says it's like fruit ripening. It doesn't take a day. First the seed has to be planted, the tree has to grow, the flowers blooming, the fruit budding. And then how to ripen the fruit? Only the sun can do that. She was indicating that sometimes we beat the fruit, yelling "Ripen! Ripen, you miserable fruit!" You know, perhaps we beat ourselves up. Only God can ripen us by shining down on us with love. What are we to do? Be present. Hang onto that tree and receive the love. Well, do you have a better idea? (laughter) It's a slow process. I wonder sometimes, how long does this take? I've been at it a whole lifetime already. In fact it takes many lifetimes. Each cell of the fruit must change to sugar. It's something only God can do.

Being a piece of ripe fruit is not for someone else's benefit. You have to live with yourself. If you are changing into sweetness, you will enjoy yourself and your life so much more. When you take the energy in and you actually heal, then everything around you is uplifted. As you chant, you draw in what you need. We are not saving the world here. We are chanting to uplift ourselves; this naturally has an effect on our environment. If you are happy, things around you will be happy. Things start rotating at a higher frequency, a faster rpm. You go around spinning faster and everyone responds to your vibration, it happens naturally.

The ending prayer says, the universe itself is complete, all the frequencies of the Universe are available, take what you need for healing, the Universe will remain whole from that taking. If you take healing from the Universe, it doesn't create a gap. There's no lack. It's continually replenished. As you take what you need from it, you become part of the whole. It becomes more beautiful through your participation in it.

Princeton, NJ concert - September 2004

class 2

(i) bellows breathing (*bhastrika pranayama*) - Lie down on the back, bring the palms on either side of the neck, being careful to place the palms underneath any hair. After the palms are flat against the side of the next, interlace the fingers behind the neck. This creates an energy seal at the top of the spine. To seal the bottom of the body, press the insides of the feet together. Now begin bellows breathing, inhaling and exhaling through the nose. This is a shallow breath, sniff in a little and sniff out. If you find you are gasping for air, concentrate on the inhale and give yourself a little more time to bring in extra air. After one minute, inhale and hold the breath, bring the navel point back towards the earth. Hold briefly, then relax the posture, bring the hands by the hips, palms facing heaven and relax.

(ii) bellows breathing - Repeat the same exercise, but this time move more air. Move as much air as you can through the body, oxygenating the blood and brain. Keep the inhale and exhale balanced, giving away as much as you take in.

(iii) one leg raise - In the same posture, raise the R leg 4 inches off the floor. Raise the head and look at the foot. Begin bellows breathing. After 15 seconds, switch legs, raising the L leg 4 inches off the floor. Keep switching two more times, then raise both legs a few inches off the floor, inhale, hold briefly, exhale and relax completely.

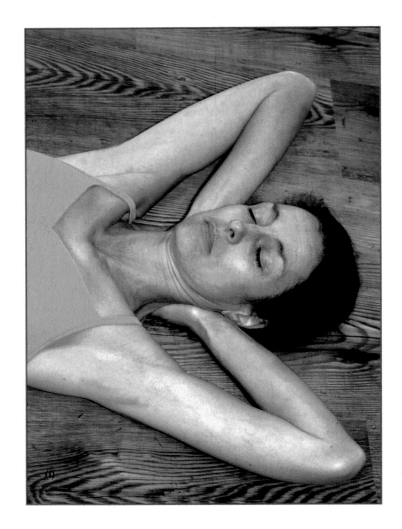

Just like a radio can dial in one station or another, your body and spirit can filter through all the frequencies and find the healing frequencies it needs.

1 pranam to prone - Sitting on the heels, bring the forehead to the floor and stretch the arms overhead. Leaving the hands where they are, come up onto all 4s and bring the heart and head down to the ground at the same time. Lift the shoulders away from the ground first, then inhale and squeeze the hands towards each other and the knees towards each other as you come up to all 4s. Exhale as you sit back on the heels and bring your forehead to the ground. Inhale as you go, exhale when you get there. 1 min. Relax on stomach breathing into the belly on the inhale, letting go on the exhale.

2 swimming - With legs straight, flutter kick the legs keeping knees and thighs off the ground. Then add the armstroke and do the freestyle stroke in swimming. Turn your head and twist to either side as you lift the arm up. 1 min. Relax on the stomach.

3 prone to cobra - Press all ten toenails into the ground, pull the shoulder blades together, even try to bring your elbows together behind you as you inhale into cobra (*bhujangasana*) and exhale lie down on your stomach. 1 min. Relax in baby pose breathing into the belly as you inhale, dumping your problems into the earth through your 3rd eye as you exhale. Then roll the head from side to side, massaging the forehead on the ground for 30 seconds.

4 pranam twist - Sit up on heels, bring the palms together, lay the L forearm along the R side of your mat, bringing head and shoulder on the ground, breathe deeply for 2 long breaths. Come up and twist to the R, bringing the R forearm alongside the L side of your mat. Press top hand into the earth to twist the spine. Do each side 2 times.

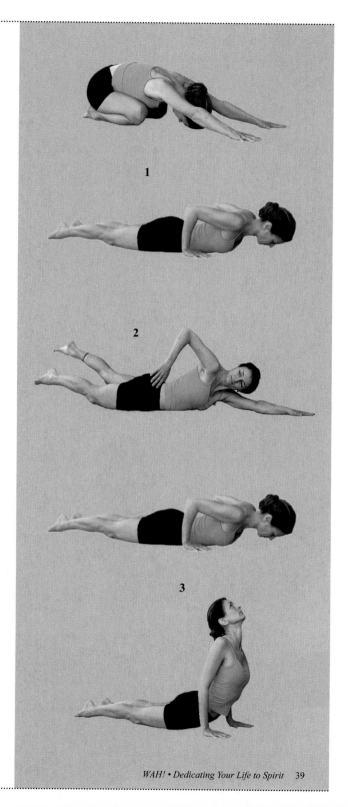

5 vinyasa through all 4s – Inhale to all 4s, exhale stomach to ground, inhale shrug shoulders up and melt the heart, exhale baby pose. Wherever your hands are in baby pose is where they should stay for the whole exercise. Spread the fingers, create a suction in the palms, press all ten toenails into the ground. Inhale as you go, exhale when you get there, 2 minutes. Relax in baby pose. You can open and close the fists to release the hands if you like.

6 rock hips side to side - In baby pose (*balasana*) rock hips side to side, if you had a pencil on your butt, you'd be drawing a smile (why does that always make people laugh?) 30 seconds, then relax in baby pose. Relax the eyes, relax the jaw. Let your problems go.

7 front stretch sitting on one heel (*paschimottanasana*) - Sit on your R heel with your L leg straight out in front of you. Hug the muscle to the bone, engaging muscular energy in the R leg. Pull the 4th and 5th toes back towards the R ear, fingertips on the ground near the hips. Inhale open the heart and bring energy in through the top of the head, exhale hinge forward bringing the rib cage onto the thigh, forehead to the ankle. 1 minute, then continue this exercise with *bhastrika pranayama* for 1 more minute. Inhale, bring your R hand to your L knee, L hand to the floor behind you and twist to the L and hold for 10-15 seconds. Exhale and switch sides.

8 walk on the sit bones - With your legs straight out in front of you, rock side to side, alternately walking the legs forward. Bend the elbows up and twist the spine as you walk forward on your sit bones. Then walk backwards. Continue 1 min.

9 bear walk – From downward facing dog, bring your weight to your R hand and foot, lifting the L foot forward and L hand forward. Place your weight on the L hand and foot, moving R foot and hand forward. Continue walking around the room. If you are blind or otherwise limited to the confines of your mat, walk on elbows and knees, keeping fists by the ears and feet by the buttocks, walking forward and back on your mat. This is **baby bear walk**.

10 hiss - Lying on your back, inhale through the nose and hiss on the exhale. Hissing increases the length of the exhale. Try to make the exhale 4 times as long as the inhale.

11 standing pranam twist (*parsva utkatasana*) - Stand with your feet together, bring your palms together at the center of your chest, bring L elbow to R knee, press R hand to the earth to twist the spine, breathe into the belly for 2 breaths. Switch sides. Repeat both sides. Pull knees together, lift toes up to engage energy moving up the legs, relax toes down but keep the energy moving up the legs. When you've finished, relax on the back.

12 two leg twist on back - Lying on back, inhale raise legs to sky, exhale bring both feet to R hand, inhale raise legs to sky, exhale lower both legs to ground. Alternate sides, keeping both shoulder blades on ground. Pull feet towards each other and hug the midline. 1 minute. Relax on the back, letting the legs fall open, hands by hips, palms facing heaven. Bring chin to L shoulder, then to R shoulder, rolling back of head on the floor.

13 hip lift - Lying on your back, press your hands and arms into the ground, draw the shoulder blades together and lift the heart to the sky. Relax down. Do a couple of times, then lift both heart and hips off the ground a couple of times, then relax.

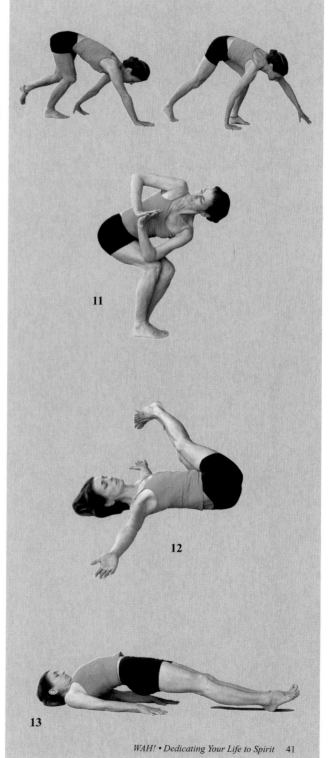

14

15

16

17

18

14 prone to plow - Hands by the hips, palms facing earth. Press the hands into the earth as you raise the legs to 90°, then overhead. Inhale as you go, exhale when your legs touch the ground on either side. Bring light in between the vertebrae as you breathe. 1 minute

15 plow (*halasana*) - Interlace fingers or place palms flat on the ground, let the shoulders rise up towards the ears, then pull the shoulder blades together. Breathe into belly. 2 minutes, then relax on back.

16 windshield wipers - Lying on back, feet by hips, drop knees to R and breathe into belly. Drop knees to L, breathe fully into belly. 3 sets.

17 caterpillar (variation) - Lying on back, soles of feet on the floor, grab opposite wrists. Lift your head and walk your shoulder blades and hips towards your feet. When your hips are close to your feet, start the other way, walking shoulder blades and hips away from your feet until your legs are straight. Continue 1 1/2 minutes

18 boat (*navasana*) - Hands 2 ft apart, legs 2 ft apart, lift arms and legs 2 ft off ground, lift head and hold for 20-30 seconds. Relax.

19 giselle jump - Come on hands and feet, bend legs and jump up, landing on hands and feet equally. Jump as high as you can. Continue 30-40 seconds, then relax on stomach.

19

20 windshield wipers on stomach - Drop your ankles L then R. 30 secs. Then start moving the feet in wide circles for **eggbeaters**, allowing the hips to rock side to side in response to the movement. Go one way and then the other. If you can't figure it out, circle one leg by itself, then circle the other before you put them together. 1 min.

21 grasshoppers - Lying on the stomach, hands underneath the shoulders, tuck the toes under. Press the feet towards each other and jump the body off the floor. You can move forward and back on your mat if you like.

22 walking firefly (*tittibhasana*) - Hold your ankles or wrap hands back around waist, walk forward and back on your feet. You can practice binding one side, then the other side; this is easy and fun. Or, if you want to try the full pose, place your hands on floor in between your feet, squeeze your legs together and raise your feet off floor.

23 donkey jumps - From downward facing dog, jump both feet up, placing the weight of your body on your hands. Do 10-15 times.

24 fish (*matseyasana*) - Sit in between the heels, hands on the soles of feet, lean back and bring forearms on the ground, melt heart to the sky and breathe long and deep for 1 1/2 min.

25 savasana

living your purpose

Living your purpose means you are internally unified by one theme, one direction. Externally, things may be disorganized, looking great or looking terrible – it doesn't matter. Living your purpose is your connection to spirit which continues regardless of what is happening in your life.

Can you choose your purpose? I don't think so. Your purpose is something you decide before you even take an incarnation. You sit with your angel, your guide, and decide on an appropriate life that will work on the weaknesses of your soul. How about a life in Michigan with one parent? Nah. A poor Russian family who leads the community? Nah. How about Cleveland with an alcoholic parent – you can learn compassion and rise above abuse - Ahh, perfect. Your purpose in life is learning and leading in a compassionate way, finding integrity in people and experiences which are less than par.

Can you change your purpose? I don't think so. Only one purpose per lifetime. Grumble all you want, yours is a lifetime of single direction. Many lessons, one goal. Align with your purpose, and your life opens up. Misalign and your spirit suffocates. For me, when I am living my purpose, every aspect of my life challenges me to grow. Sometimes when my external life is falling apart, I feel my purpose more strongly.

When I was younger, I was quite proud of the yoga and meditation I had accomplished. I felt I was living my purpose. I had joined an ashram – they had given me superior techniques to practice asana and meditation. I was told where to go, when to sleep, what to eat, who to marry, and how to be. So I didn't have to decide anything. It was easy, in a way – I couldn't take credit or blame for anything. "Ah you are wonderful!" Yes, this is my Guru's doing. Well, "You are a mess!" was also a reflection of my Guru, and his ongoing work with me. In some ways, I was living my teacher's purpose more than my own. I put myself into the teacher training system and became a star student. I didn't really find myself; I found a system. However, it was an integral and valuable part of my self-discovery.

People confide in me privately, "I wish I had gotten into yoga sooner." I don't believe this. You can't edit your life, changing the order of circumstances and experiences. Each person's discovery process is perfect and complete exactly as it unfolds. You wanted it sooner? I don't think so. You had other things to experience first, so you could be open to learning the yoga now. Or so you could be open to the relationship or job or whatever your current situation is.

I didn't find my purpose and live it. I lived it, and my purpose became defined by my living it. I didn't start my life saying "I'm going to learn yoga and meditation." My past lifetimes brought me to it. To be honest, I couldn't find any job that would stick. The earth was boring to me. At age seven, I was reading minds. It drove my parents crazy. "How does she know that? She wasn't there when we talked about that." I was a curious, thirsty child. As an adult, I am still driven by a thirst for spiritual understanding. Does it have a name? Let me ask you, does it *need* to have a name? One day as I was talking with Alison Granucci, the program director at Omega Institute, she said,

"Wah!, this is not a 9-5 job for you is it? It seems you have dedicated your whole life to spirit." And so we called my retreats Dedicating Your Life to Spirit. Could I have come up with a name for my purpose? Definitely not. Only sports commentators can give play by play narration. My job is to live it.

I went and found a Guru because I wanted my karmas to be finished. I saw an astrologer and he said, "What are you doing?! You are trying to finish everything in this lifetime? You are doing eleven lifetimes in one. Your teacher is only doing three. What is your hurry?" I said, "I'm going to get liberated. I'm going to get off the planet! Ha *ha*!" And he said, "Hmmm, no I don't think so. You have many more lifetimes after this." "Oh." Well, that burst my bubble. And then what was my hurry? As I started to relax, it got really difficult. I had to live with myself and my idiosyncrasies.

There is no right way to live this life. There is no right way to practice yoga or chanting. There is no right way to secure Wall Street. You will not win at Monopoly every time. It's a play. The sequence of your life is something you created to instigate the most growth in you. Success has nothing to do with it.

Certain things you hold dear. It's just the way it is. You are attracted to some things and other things don't hold your attention. If something triggers a reaction, there's something there for you to discover. An experience could trigger love or anger, it's still a reaction. Look into that. There's something there.

Your triggers will be different than mine. I'm always looking for something. I have to learn to find nothing. The more I get to nothing, the better it is. But for me that's scary. I want to have 12 steps, so at least I can know what step I'm on. I want to do Series I or Series II, be a teacher or a student. It's not possible. I am just walking, traveling, meeting people. Sharing my experience and listening to others. Is this a purpose? I think it is. The more I live it, the more I open up to what it is.

You might think you know what you are doing. You might be going to school, getting a degree, or teaching yoga. It doesn't matter. All that will change. Listen to your heartfelt desires. They will lead you beyond your definitions. Better to say 'I am going' and nothing more. Allow yourself to come forward in full expression. It's permission to be whoever you are. And then you will see how it all ties together to reveal your unique purpose in this life.

Journey Magazine - August 2005

With open arms you greet me and I feel the spirit rise.
With open heart you hold me and I come to realize
The door of my heart is opening,
And everywhere I look I see love rushing.

class 3

(i) shakti bandha - Sit on heels, exhale all the air out, inhale deeply and hold the breath, bend forward in yoga mudra and swing arms side to side. Keep the forehead on the ground. The ribs are not touching the thighs, so you can twist fully. Exhale and come sitting up. Do this 4 times.

(ii) 4 part breathing - Inhale in four parts and hold four parts, press the air out, out, out, and out, hold the breath out for four parts, create a suction in the body without changing the breath. Then suck the air in, in, in, and in. Hold the breath in and mentally press out in all directions (up, down, left, right, front and back). Then press the air out, out, out, out. Keep going in this way for 4 minutes.

(iii) tongue roll - Sitting in easy pose, bring the tongue outside the teeth but inside the lips and make as wide a circle as you can with your tongue. Continue for 1 minute, then nurse on the tongue for 1 minute.

(vi) massage - Moving fingertips and thumbtips in circles, massage the chest, armpit, behind shoulder, neck and shoulder muscle (trapezius). 30 secs each side. Repeat in the other direction and rest.

(i)

When you refine and purify your energetic channels (nadis), you become more sensitive. Staying connected to higher Self helps you decide which things to welcome into your life and which things to distance yourself from. The mind can draw in the healing frequencies it needs. Healing frequencies feel pleasant and natural. Energies that support you are familiar, as if you always felt that way. Healing frequencies do not use exertion - you cannot "try" to heal. In healing, you are returned to your natural state, existing in a frequency you know and understand. The miracle is not becoming something amazing; the miracle is living and relishing who you are.

1 dynamic sitting twist - Sitting in a comfortable position, hands on shoulders, fingers in front, thumbs in back, inhale twist L, exhale twist R. 1 1/2 min.

2 forward stretch (*paschimottanasana*) - Inhale up, exhale bow forward. 1 min. Then add arm (same as straight leg) extending overhead, drawing in what you need from the Universe through the breath and hand. 1 min.

3 extended child pose (*uttitha balasana*) - Sitting on heels, lower rib cage til it's just off the thighs, straighten spine, find a spot on the floor to look at, begin *bhastrika pranayama.* 1 min.

4 front lunge - Squeeze legs towards each other, palms together at center of chest, expand the back of the body as you breathe into belly. Then extend the exhale and watch belly pull towards spine at end of exhale. Do each side twice.

5 water buckets (dynamic *marichyasana*) - From *marichyasana*, lift the body off the ground balancing on one hand and one foot, pull the thigh to the rib cage, inner spiral the legs and lift the hips up. You can either rise up off the ground, or for more challenge, raise the hips up until both legs are straight, you are stepping on one hand. Inhale up, exhale down, 1 1/2 min.

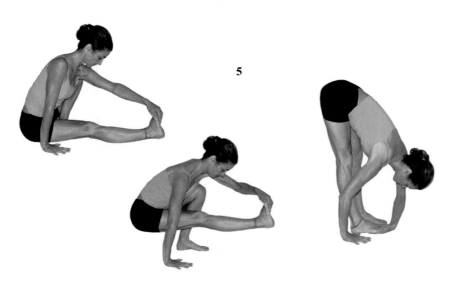

5

1

2

3

4

6 swing (*lolasana*) - With legs straight out in front of you, hands by hips, lift body up and scoot forward 4x, scoot backwards 4x. Then cross legs in half lotus or full lotus and scoot forward and back for 30 more seconds.

7 locust pose (*shalabhasana*) - Tuck toes under, hands in fists at the thigh crease or palms flat on floor, alternate leg lifts 1 min. Then inhale lift both legs up, exhale down for 20 seconds, inhale lift and hold, relax.

8 cry baby - Lying on stomach, beat forearms and tops of feet on the earth, lift head off the ground. Yelling or crying is helpful to get the energy moving up the spine. 1 min.

9 half locust twist (*parsva ardha shalabhasana*) - From locust pose, extend hands out to sides to make a cross, tuck toes under, raise R leg, touch L hand, alternate sides. 1 1/2 min.

10 inchworm - Lying on stomach, hands by the hips, inch forward and back. 1 min.

11 windshield wipers - Lying on stomach, bend knees up and drop both ankles to L, and to R, 30 seconds

12 body drops - Lying on stomach, hands under shoulders, lift body up and drop down on the rib cage, gently but with enough force to create a change. 45 seconds

13 extended locust (*salabhasana* variation) - Palms joined over head, inhale and stretch hands, head and feet up, exhale and lower down. Move slowly, integrate light into the body on the inhale, exhale let go of what you don't need. 1 min.

14 baby pose - Come into baby pose and spread the knees wide, bringing heart towards the earth. Turn one cheek to the floor and breathe into belly. 1 min.

15 walking on air - Lying on your back, raise R arm and L leg to sky and lower to ground, raise L arm and R leg to sky and lower, inhale up, exhale lower leg and arm. 1 1/2 min.

16 sitting twist - Sitting in between the heels *(virasana)*, lean back and place the L hand directly behind you, about 12" away from the body, fingers point to the R, swing R hand to meet L, as if the fingers would meet, and twist the spine. Swing R and L, using hand on the floor to create more twist in spine. 1 min.

17 cat and cow - Inhale bring belly towards earth, exhale bring belly towards heaven. Head responds to movement of spine. Continue for 1 minute, then lift feet off ground and circle ankles as you continue cat and cow.

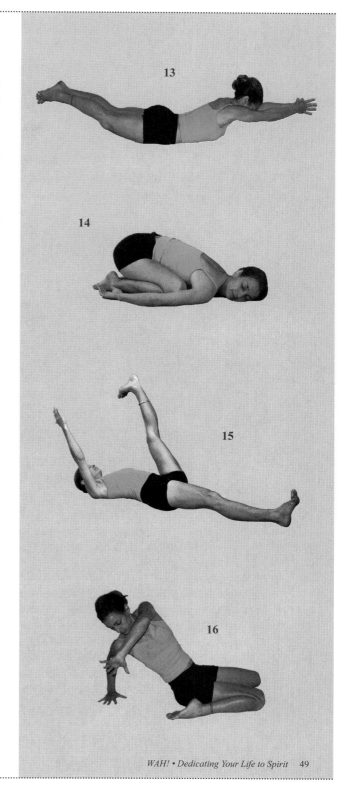

18

19

21

18 prone to baby pose - You can do this exercise with the following variations - (a) palms flat on the ground, (b) on the mounds of the fingers, heels of the hands raised, pressing through the 1st and 2nd fingers, and/or (c) on the fingertips. 1 1/2 minutes

19 cow variation (*marjaryasana*) - From all 4s, extend leg behind you, circle leg clockwise then counter-clockwise inhale through nose, exhale stick tongue out and breathe out through mouth, widen or cross the eyes in lion breath (*simha pranayama*). 30 seconds, switch sides, repeat.

20 side angle lift from forearm (*vasishtasana*) - Lie on your side, palm parallel to top of mat. Press palm into floor, draw elbow and foot towards each other, lifting hips up. Take 2 full breaths, relax down. Repeat. For added challenge, grab hold of foot and raise one leg up.

21 isometric stretch on back - Lying on back, grab hold of foot and pull foot towards chest. Press foot into hands and create an isometric tension. Breathe deeply, 30 seconds each side.

20

22

22 jump throughs - Lie on your back, come sitting up, place hands on either side of your hips, walk or jump feet back and lie on stomach. Then walk or jump feet up to hands, sit down, lie down on back. Continue 1 1/2 min.

23 bridge (*setu bandhasana*) - Lie on your back, press back of arms into earth and melt the heart towards heaven, inner spiral the legs and raise the hips into the spaciousness you just created with the inner spiral, melt the heart by squeezing shoulder blades together, press the back of the head into earth, take a few deep breaths in the posture, and relax down. Do 5 times.

24 backbend (*urdhva dhanurasana*) - Bring your head near a wall, place hands on either side of head, wrists facing wall. Inner spiral the legs and raise hips up, come onto top of head, bring elbows to the wall (disconnected), bring elbows away from the wall (shoulder blades connecting into back, melting the heart), and come up into backbend. Straighten arms and press through 1st and 2nd finger knuckles. Breathe into belly, come down when ready. Do 3 times.

25 savasana

23

25

24

working on yourself

Perhaps you have seen Tibetan prayer wheels in a temple somewhere. Large cylindrical tubes stand in a line, each one with a prayer carved into it. Handles on the bottom of the tubes allow people to turn the wheels as they pass by. When the wheels turn, the prayers that are written on them are spoken by the wind. *Om Mani Padme Hum* or May All Beings Live in Peace is initiated by spinning the prayer wheel, and the Universe speaks those words.

Oftentimes, the wheels are set up in a row. You can spin one prayer, then the next, and the next, and so on down the line. You can spin each prayer wheel in that row. Sometimes by the time you are finished the row, your first prayer wheel has stopped spinning, so you can go back to the top of the line and start in again.

I think of these prayer wheels like *chakras*. As I teach, and sing, and meditate with people, it's as if I am going around the room spinning the *chakras* of each person. By the time I am finished one side, it's time to go back and start again with the first person. In the body, each wheel corresponds to a *chakra*, an energy center. If all the *chakras* are rotating and moving, the person is happy and growing. The practice of chanting, yoga or meditation is a process of getting all those eight wheels (*chakras*) to spin. If they're not spinning, then you're not present on some level. The idea is to have them all spinning.

I tell people the most important work you can do as a teacher is to work on yourself. You can only take your students as far as you have gone yourself. In this field of spiritual work, it's a matter of finding others who seek light and hanging out with them. In the same way that you seek to improve your game of tennis by playing with other people, a spiritual aspirant will seek others to practice and meditate with, to learn from, to share. Each of us carries someone along; each of us has someone who is depending on us to care for them – our children, our family, a co-worker, a person on the street. The Universe is an interconnected web of people helping other people. We grow through being there for them, helping them, giving them love and nurturance. And there is always a being higher than you willing to help you forward. It's an interconnected web; there's always someone below you and above you.

All these techniques draw you into a healing space. That healing space is The Void, where all things come from and dissolve back to. I laugh when I hear certain teachers say that their yoga postures, mudras and meditations are special because they were channeled or revealed to them in meditation. Give me a break! It's *all* revealed; that's how these techniques came forth. And because they originated in the void, they naturally take you back there when you practice them. Practicing any yogic or meditative technique will necessarily reveal its teaching to you. It's built-in. You can relax, knowing that whatever practice you are involved in will lead you to absorption in the cosmic element. It doesn't have to be the right path, it only has to be the path you are on. If you take it with love, it will lead you.

What to do when you're not present? When you're not feeling connected? Stay still. If you notice that you are not present when you are teaching, take a pause. Take a moment. If you're not present when you're home, sit down.

Take a moment. Just noticing that an area of your life is at a standstill will help activate it again. The body will heal itself. All it needs is the space in which to do it. You provide the space.

Perhaps you have noticed that the prayer wheels don't go anywhere. They circle around and around. The energy stays within. So too, in our practice – there is no energy created or destroyed. We simply evolve within its flow. We adopt certain aspects and experiences in order to grow, and then we surrender them back to the void. Nothing is stationary; everything is borrowed. And it all turns like that wheel.

So don't feel that you have to create something – a style of teaching, or a new yoga center, or a change in your job or relationship. You don't have to do anything. Just show up. As the energy mixes with who you are, the change happens. It's a flow. It naturally leads you to what you should be doing. We don't create all this stuff; we participate in it. It changes us, and that's a real privilege.

Look at how this yoga center was created – at first there was a yoga center on the other side of town. Then it dissolved and that energy came here. Now it's a community which is growing and thriving on its own. Could Julie create this center? No. The energy collected here and Julie was happy to open herself to the role of "yoga center owner." It was a flow, a powerful current. Have you ever tried to move the waves in the ocean? You should try sometime, just to see how silly it feels. No, you can't direct the flow; you have to move with the current, the divine energy of the Universe. And participate in it.

You don't need to find what to do. It's already happening. As soon as you unroll your mat, you find out who you are that day. It all comes rushing at you. You might be tired, or energetic, or nervous, or whatever the case may be. You notice who you are and engage your energies. Try to get all seven chakras rotating, fully awakened and alive. This is what I think about when I chant or teach yoga.

Healing happens in the void. There are layers to get to the void – anger, integration, awareness, etc. But until you get to the void, there is no healing. The practices help you descend from conscious effort into the void. There are elements of technique - how your body is aligned, how your breath functions, how you let go in *savasana*, how you surrender to the *mantra*. But besides that is an understanding that all these techniques came from the void in the first place, and they will naturally guide you back to it. These techniques were revealed. A group of yogis got together and decided to hide themselves from traditional ritualistic forms of religion and practice various techniques to see what they really do. They experimented – through fasting, through narrowing the focus of attention, the techniques were revealed to them. We who practice these techniques are naturally led back to the Source.

The things that block us from being in the void are our emotional stuff, our karmas and blockages. Injuries are great that way. You don't think you're blocked. But then the injury shows where your weakness was. It couldn't withstand pressure. The injury is probably something that was weak in the first place, something that you needed to work on, some hidden agenda that you weren't noticing. You cover it up, you over-compensate with other muscles and behavior patterns. Sooner or later, the issue comes up for you to work on. The blockage hurts. It keeps you from experiencing the cosmos. So you have to work on it. You have to get it back in alignment; you have to get your life back into alignment and then - whoa - you're back in the flow.

The quickest way to get rid of your stuff is to recycle the energy. Take the example from the prayer wheel. The *mantra* continues rotating; it cycles back in on itself. All the *mantras* cycle. The tongue cycles in the mouth. The energy doesn't go anywhere. The energy builds on itself. It collects and multiplies until it affects a visible change. And the process becomes your journey.

In your teacher training you have learned about the *shatkarmas* – some physical purifications you can do for the body to make it a clean vessel. So you may know about *amoroli*, or urine therapy. This is the same principle as *mantra* chanting. Some yogis collect the urine first thing in the morning and drink a portion of it. They take what's coming out and return it back to the system. Not everything. They are not drinking their urine all day long – only a small piece of it – that time just before waking when the minerals collect, when the dreams reveal the subconscious thoughts – they take that energy and recycle it back. Take your deepest, darkest secrets and eat them for breakfast. It's the same with *mantra* chanting. You take the *mantra* and repeat it and the thoughts that surface in the mind get recycled. Whether you are looking at the present, at something that happened today, at something that happened last week, or even in childhood doesn't matter. Whatever thoughts you have are re-ingested into the system. This cycling process continues until the thoughts dissolve; they no longer surface as an issue, or a blockage. Eventually you get to the void and bask there. This is where the healing takes place: on the way there and as you arrive.

The teachers and guides don't look for outward success. They feed you experiences that cause your energy to recycle at a more rapid rate. It's not a comfortable moment! Look at it this way: When you are in warrior pose, you must stay there for five breaths. What happens? "Oh god, when is this going to be over?" or "Look at that lady over there, her knee is not over her toe, she's not doing it right!" Do you understand how much stuff comes up when you hold that posture and recycle your energy? If you could move, you would move away from those thoughts. But you can't, so the thoughts recycle and you examine them. You breathe. You watch. You breathe. And then you move to the next pose. Do you see how these small moments recycle the energy? This is the main difference between yoga and aerobics. For me, much of my understanding comes from my experience of this recycling principle.

The people I hang out with are connected to the void more than they are connected to the world. If I ask my friend if he's coming, he will say, "Let me ask my guides." Another friend looks at billboards, which send him messages like, "We haven't forgotten about you." They have active conversations with Source energy, all day long.

Well, if you are not connected to the void, you're connected to the world. Which do you prefer? Instead of asking your guides, you are asking your friends, your parents, or if your parents are not there you might ask the voice of your parents living in your head, or your teacher, or your boss. It's all worldly advice, opinions and judgment calls; it's not you. Healing happens in the silence when you surrender to the greater Self that is, your own Self, your piece of the whole infinite cosmic puzzle. And until you surrender yourself into that space, how will anything be revealed? My speciality is chanting – I come together with people, see how their wheels are spinning, and then ask them to jump off the cliff with me, into the void. What will happen? I don't know. I don't presume to know. It's beyond me. I can't access it through my intelligence, so I must access it through my intuition. I ask everyone here to come with me.

When I tour, I meet with people maybe once a year. I always ask them, "What have you found?" Where has the healing taken you? What did you discover in your process? I really want to know. It's not a line. If the process takes you into the void, I want to know what happened as a result. Perhaps the marriage fell apart or the business collapsed; perhaps a new beginning, a new venture, or a baby has come. The void springs infinite possibilities, all of them I believe lead to joy.

It's a series of readjustments and realignments. Getting to the void is the key thing, and after awhile the readjustments don't bother you so much anymore. You acknowledge them for what they are: readjusting your orientation. Amma says, "It is not possible to measure one's spiritual growth by observing external actions. However, spiritual advancement can be understood to some degree by observing one's reactions to adverse circumstances."

For me, the practice is opening. Opening to the void. I look forward to my time in practice. It feeds me. I want to rush to the void. If you are a teacher, you know. The energy gets to flow through you. You no longer teach from your head about all the things you've learned; you teach from your heart. It's an opening you experience together, teacher and student. Everyone benefits. And it's the most fun. If you are genuinely present with your students, they are getting a taste of what the void is. It's a positive experience. You are surrendering to being yourself. It's a great example.

As you teach you're not always going to be spot-on. Your own life will be a platform for growth. Your marriage might fall apart, you might have lawsuits, various adjustments to your personal outlook. Showing how the process works is invaluable. How to deal with a cog in the wheel, how to deal with things that get caught in your energy field. It's not a role of perfection you're striving for. It's an example of compassion. Let the process be done in first person. Be present, seek the void and allow what comes from it to be shared with open arms and open heart.

Manhattan Beach, CA   Mukti Yoga Teacher Training - December 2004

class 4

(i) side stretch - Sitting in easy pose, press L forearm or elbow against L knee and raise R arm overhead, leaning back and twisting to the R. Switch sides, continue alternating slowly for 1 minute.

(ii) massage lymph glands at neck - With first two fingers, vigorously massage the indentation where the ear and lower jaw meet, moving in circles or side-to-side. Dig in 5-10 times then gently drag the fingers an inch or two down the side of the neck following the drainage lines of the lymph glands, 30 seconds each side. Repeat.

(iii) massage lymph glands at jaw - Press 2nd and 3rd fingers under the jaw pushing up and back towards the tongue, moving in small circles. Gently drag the fingers down the front of the neck. This is a gentler movement than the previous exercise. 30 seconds each side. Repeat.

(iv) neck massage - Reach R hand around back of neck, squeeze fingers to heel of hand as your fingers gently slide over neck vertebrae. Do same with L hand.

(v) dig for gold - Sitting in easy pose, hands at the waistline, fingers in front, thumbs in back, dig the fingers into the abdomen and see what you find (breakfast perhaps), massage above the navel, to the sides of the navel, and below the navel, leave the thumbs in back. 1 min.

(i)

The more refined something is, the more quickly its molecules vibrate. Solid matter has molecules that move slowly; liquid molecules move more quickly; and gaseous or etheric molecules move the quickest. You bring light in on the inhale because it can move through your system and speed up any frequencies which are rotating slowly. Dense energies are indications of slowly moving molecules. The body is 98% water; everything should be moving and changing with that speed. As you become more proficient in absorbing healing light and processing your issues, you will be asked to process change at an increasingly rapid rate.

1 leg circle - From all 4s, extend R leg straight behind you, circle leg clockwise for 20 secs, extend L leg and circle counter-clockwise, 20 secs each side.

2 alternate extension - From all 4s, extend the L arm forward and the R leg back on the inhale, exhale and lower, continue alternating sides, 1 min.

3 leg circle, opposite direction - From all 4s, extend R leg circle counter-clockwise 20 secs, extend L leg circle clockwise for 20 secs. Rest in baby pose.

4 prone to pranam - From baby pose (*balasana/pranamasana*), inhale to all 4s, exhale bring stomach to ground, inhale to all 4s, exhale to baby pose. Continue 1 min.

5 rock hips side to side - In baby pose, bring hands by feet, palms facing heaven. Rock hips side to side, if you had a pencil on your butt, you'd draw a smile. 30 seconds, then relax in baby pose. Relax the eyes, relax the jaw. Let your problems go.

6 pranam twist - Sitting on heels, press palms together and bring your R elbow to L knee and lay your head and shoulder on the ground, breathing deeply for 2 long breaths. Come up and twist to the R, bringing L elbow to R knee. Press top hand into the earth to twist the spine, elbows will widen. Do each side 2 times.

7 inchworm - Lying on stomach, hands by hips, chin on ground. Raise hips up and drop them to the floor, 30 secs.

8 alternate inchworm - Raise L hip, then R hip, rocking side to side, 30 secs.

9 body beats - Lying on stomach, make fists of the hands and beat the hips and outer thighs. Continue beating and move up to waist and sides of rib cage. Move up to shoulder blades or whatever you can reach. Beat back of waist, then thighs, then relax.

10 one legged twisting bow pose (*ek pada parsva dhanurasana*) - Lying on stomach, extend R arm overhead palm flat on the floor, bend R leg and grab ankle with L hand, arch up into one-legged bow, pulling the arm extended in front of you back towards the body, take at least one full breath before lowering and doing the other side. Alternate from side to side for 1 min.

11 sidewinder - Lying on stomach, chin on the ground, hands by the hips, palms facing heaven. Lift the hips up and move them to the right, then lift feet, head and shoulders to the right and come back into alignment. Move sideways to the right, then sideways to the left, travelling like a sidewinder snake. 2 min.

12 forearm plank - Come up and hold for 15 seconds, relax down. Repeat one more time.

13 rocking bow (*dhanurasana*) - Rocking side to side, bring R toes to ground when you rock to the R, L toes to ground when you rock to L. Try to bring top leg closer to ground to stretch chest. 1 min.

14 grasshopper jumps - Raise body and drop down onto rib cage for body drops, then try to jump whole body off the floor including hands, total 1 min.

15 body beats - Lie down on the back. Using the inside of the fists or fingertips, softly beat the lower abdomen (let the fist fall on the belly with a thud). Move up to the area above the navel. Then move up to the chest, using the R fist to beat the L side of the chest, and then switch and use the L fist to beat the R side. Then use both fists on either side of the chest and make a sound as you beat - You can say "Ah!" or give a Tarzan yell if you like. Keep the fists relaxed, work your way down to the waist, upper abdomen, lower abdomen, then rest.

Relax on the back, inhale through the nose, exhale through the mouth on "Ah!" Visualize ash floating out of the mouth as you exhale. Make the exhale as long as you can. Conjure up all your toxins on the inhale and let them fly out your mouth naturally on the exhale. If you saw the movie "Green Mile" you might remember the healer releasing ash from his mouth after he healed someone. This is the same practice, only we are healing ourselves today.

> ***about body beats*** - *Bones respond to pressure by adding osteoblasts, or bone-forming cells, which boost the density of the bone. Weight-bearing exercise is considered the best therapy for bones - running, walking, handstands, arm balances. But pressure can be applied in other ways, not just lengthwise but also laterally. Body beats and body drops are an alternative method to stimulating bone and body tissue.*

16 walking on air - Lying on the back, alternately bring one leg up to the sky and lower it. Add the opposite arm when you are ready. R leg and L arm raise and lower together, L leg and R arm. Keep them parallel as you move. 1 1/2 min.

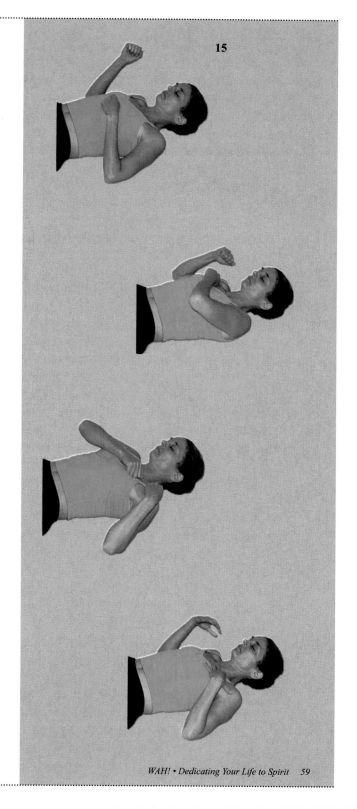

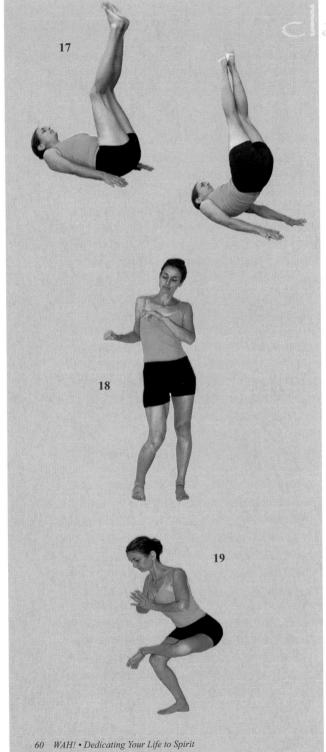

17 downhill ski - Lying on back, legs to 90°, hugging feet to midline, knees bent. Hands are by hips, palms facing earth. Press backs of hands and arms into the earth and raise hips high off the ground, twist hips and lower them near the R hand. Raise hips again, twist and lower to L hand. Continue alternating side to side, 2 min.

18 standing twist - Come standing up with feet a little more than hip width apart, bend elbows up and twist the hips side to side. Put on some dance music and twist to the rhythm of the music. 2 min. Rest in a standing position, shaking shoulders and hands or whatever feels comfortable, then twist again for 2 min.

19 awkward chair (*utkatasana*) variation - From standing, bring the L ankle to the R knee, bend R knee, hands in prayer pose, 2 full breaths, come up and switch sides. Repeat.

20 crow (*bakasana*) - Both feet on ground, bend forward and place hands on the ground, bring knees into armpits, bring weight of body onto hands as you press the insides of the feet together. Look at the ground. For more challenge, practice **flying pigeon** (*eka pada galavasana*) - as in the previous pose, bring the L ankle to the R knee, bend forward and place arms on the ground, bringing the L knee to L armpit and R foot to R armpit, activate toes to engage inner spiral, hips move up to the sky.

21 alternate toe touches - Stand with your feet wide and isometrically draw feet towards midline. Extend arms out to sides, spreading fingers to engage energy towards the heart. Bring R hand to L foot or outside L foot, twisting spine and looking L up to sky. Continue alternating side to side, 1 min.

22 standing zip wash - Grab opposite wrists and twist the hips vigorously, shaking abdominal organs as well as buttocks, 30 secs.

23 locust pose (*shalabasana*) - Lying on stomach, hands and feet together, inhale up, exhale down. 30 secs.

24 savasana

presence

The presence of bliss has existed before you or me; existed before time and space; and is the source of all souls, energy and matter. When we meditate we dip into this presence. It is the source of all healing. My karmas are what come between me and my capacity to sit in bliss as a constant presence. Ah lovely karmas! This is my work to do. When karmas are smooth, marriage is going well, job is good, there is not much internal growth. When the money is there, nobody fights. When the money is gone, everybody fights. When the money is gone, the real work begins. You don't see the issues when life is cushioned. The money glosses everything over so you can't see the karmas so easily. When the money is drained away or Saturn returns in your astrological chart, then it etches away some of that glossiness and you are able to see, sometimes for the first time, whoa! I have a lot of work to do! Me, I thought I was perfect. I was so shocked at how much I had to work on internally – how insecure, how much self-hatred and doubt I had.

The only way to be in bliss while occupying a body is by transforming every moment, no matter what you are doing. The people in your life are part of the program. The jobs, shortfalls and outcomes are also part of the program. Do the work in front of you, do it with love. What a wonderful process, to drop into an infinite space and allow yourself to be worked on, loosened, opened. Maybe you drop into an infinite space through meditation, or maybe a disaster takes you there, what's the difference? You might feel afraid to experience the disaster, like you don't want to suffer or look at yourself. You think, "Oh there's nothing wrong." That feels safe, at least. "Everything's fine. Things couldn't be better!" (laughter) Well, this is a path of awareness. Looking at yourself is scary at first – ok, it's scary all the time – but it does lead to greater understanding, widens your heart and brings you closer to oneness with all that there is.

The saints are so absorbed in this presence, they don't even have names. Every lady saint is called Amma. So how would you know which one? The guy saints are "Baba" Which Baba? Sai Baba? Which Sai Baba? Shirdi Sai Baba? Satya Sai Baba? Neem Karoli Baba? Everyone's a Baba. It means father. Amma means mother. These beings are absorbed in the bliss state; they don't care about names. For our own purposes, we give them nicknames so we can know which one is which. They are like email addresses at yahoo or aol – if the name is already taken, you have to come up with another name so the email goes through. So there's Amma and Divine Amma and Ananda Ma and Anandamayi Ma and Amritanandamayi Ma and Karuna Ma and Shree Ma. It's ridiculous. They all mean the same thing! They are code names we use to identify them. After all, you don't want the email to bounce when you need to reach one of them.

The saints are like an older brother or sister who has already been on the path you are taking. They can help you get there without so many wrong turns. They meditated to get there, and you will meditate to get there too. You have to do the work. But it's nice to have some company along the way. And it's not a marked path, let me tell you. There is no single path to God. You will not walk the same path as your teacher walked. They are not asking you to walk their path, they are just showing you where the light is. There are a million paths to God and yours will be walked only by you in your unique way. To be honest, I'm not really sure what these saints do. At Amma's programs, She greets each person in the room individually. One by one. Yes, there is a lecture, a meditation program and some chanting; but greeting three to five thousand people takes a long time. Sometimes the programs last 18 hours or so. So the rest of us get hungry and tired and need something to do. So in the back of the hall, there's shopping, videos of the charity programs, places for people to talk. In various rooms, people are chopping vegetables, selling food, others are talking, someone is freaking out. In the midst of all this milling around, Amma is greeting each person.

She monitors the energy of what's happening in the room and that's how She works on us. One time She asked us to put one foot of space between all the chairs in the hall. What?! That was about 2,000 chairs. "She says make sure no chair is touching any other chair. Make 12" of space around each chair." We were in a hotel ballroom. The chairs were locked together in neat orderly rows, so we had to unlock all the chairs and then spread them out. It seemed pointless. But actually it changed the energy in the room substantially. Instead of people side stepping their way down a church pew, they waltzed in and out of the rows, set up places to talk, hang out, it became more like a living room. It was really cozy. She works on us like this. She changes the lights, calls you here or there, oh and by the way, can you go and get the person on parking level 2? He's freaking out, bring him back in. So you go to parking level 2 and sure enough, there's some guy freaking out. "Mother has said come back." He cries; you bring him back.

How to describe presence? It's a big melting pot where everything comes in and recycles out in a different way in perfect divinity. It's unexplainable. It's as if this presence is the altar of change. We have these altars. We sit in front of them. The idea is to have some medium of exchange, some place to transform ourselves. You can sit at your altar and dip into bliss, ask for what you need, exchange ideas and challenges.

We love these saints, these beings that have no form. We give them names, we give them titles. We give them form. The titles get longer and longer the more they hang around here on earth. Amma was *Amritanandamayi Ma*, then *Mata Amritanandamayi Ma*, the next year it was *Shri Mata Amritanandamayi Ma*, last I heard it was *Shri Mata Amritanandamayi Ma Devi*… maybe next year it will be *Shri Shri Shri Mata Amritanandamayi Ma Devi* (laughter). We can't help ourselves, we try to describe what that is. Everytime we move into bliss state with that saint, we long to describe what that experience is. So the name gets longer, more incredible. The saints have to drop their body and reincarnate just to get a shorter name again. (laughter)

We long to describe this presence, and yet it cannot be done. We hang out with a saint, it blows our mind. What the heck was that all about? I'll tell you, that's when you know you have reached bliss. When you can't say a single word. It's indescribable. All the names you will chant tonight are words of praise like this. *Jai, Jaya, He, Shri, Wah*… My name is what you say just before you go into *Samadhi*, the expression of indescribable perfection. All the words mean this. Because what are you going to say when you reach the void? "Yes, this is very nice." No, you're not going to be able to say anything. Your brain will turn off, unable to describe. So you just say, "Wow." That's what *Jai, Jaya, He, Shri* and *Wah* all mean. When you sit in this presence, you can only say, "*Wahhhhh…*" (tipping head back, raising arm up) and jump to another plane of existence.

Prescott, Phoenix, Tucson, AZ concerts - January 2005

guidelines for savasana

Your most important instruction in this pose is not moving a muscle. The body is dead. Do not engage brain or body. It is best if you are not touching anyone else. Even if accidentally nudged by a child or someone walking by, it is important to bear no reaction. Muscles are limp. The body should be in a comfortable position to relax. You can put a bolster or rolled blanket under your knees if you like. Cover your body with a blanket or shawl. Cover your eyes with a cloth or lavender-filled eye pillow. Relax arms by the sides, palms facing heaven. Close your eyes and follow the breath. Watch the rib cage rise and fall as the breath enters and exits the body ... Then follow one of the visualizations for healing and rejuvenation.

---

assisted preparation for savasana

Stand with your feet on either side of your partner's ankles. Grab your partner's ankles from underneath and slowly lift both feet, swinging them from side to side about 5 or 6 times. Pull feet gently away from body as you lower them to floor.

Stand by your partner's shoulder and grab your partner's wrist, gently shaking it side to side. As you jiggle the wrist, the arm will respond in a ripple motion. Then hold your partner's fingers with both hands and gently pull the fingers, palm and thumb away from the body as you bring the arm to rest on the floor. This can be enhanced by using your foot or other hand to secure the shoulder to the ground, so the spine doesn't come out of alignment when you pull the hand away from the body. Do both sides.

Stand by your partner's head and lift it with both hands, rolling it slowly and gently from side to side, forward and back. Pull the base of the skull away from the spine as you lower head to floor.

---

solo preparation for savasana

Lift one leg, gently drop it down
Lift other leg, gently drop it down
Lift each arm and gently drop it down
Roll chin to R shoulder, then L shoulder, moving slowly to relax the head and neck

visualizations for savasana
(yoga nidra)

Prepare yourself for *savasana*. Close the eyes, feel the body become heavy. Slowly sink into the earth, relaxing the eyes and face. Find your breath and observe it rising and falling. Place your body in an imaginary healing ceremony and watch yourself work as a healer. Begin dismantling the body. Take the feet and throw them away. Toss your shins and thighs into a pile. Let the vertebrae unleash. Throw each vertebra into a vat of healing liquid. Take the ribs, the floating ribs and connected ribs and throw each of them aside. Remove your intestines, take them out and inspect them. Remove the bladder, kidneys and sexual organs. Scrub everything clean. Take the liver out and toss it in the healing vat. Remove the arms, hands and fingers. Immerse them and scrub them clean. Take the skull out, examine it - this is what the *sadhus* use as their eating and drinking bowl. Take the brain matter and offer it up for healing. Wash the inside of the skull. When you are done, slowly take each piece out of the healing vat and toss it towards your body, allowing the magnetism of spirit to rebuild and shape your body.

Place yourself in a beautiful and comfortable setting. You can choose a favorite childhood place or recall a memorable vacation spot, or simply remember the last time you shared a cozy space with yourself or someone else. Find a sunny rock or bed of warm sand to lie on. Begin to heal the body by infusing empty spaces with light. At the juncture of all 52 bones in your feet, sprinkle the dust of healing light. Where the feet meet the ankles, start a dance of energy. At the shins and knees play with the moving particles. Start creating the Milky Way, like so many stars in your body. Become a thousand points of dancing light. At the thighs... where the sacrum meets the spine... in between each vertebra... Where the spine meets the rib cage, make the light dance. Where the collar bones meet the shoulders, create solar systems, stars and planets. At the elbows... forearms.... wrists... send lightbeams through the bone and muscle tissue. Bring light in into each fingertip... shoulder blades... top of the spine.... skull... lips... eyelids... ears... Where the skin touches the ground. Become light. Stay only with the breath. Let the body dance in the ethers.

visualizations for savasana
(yoga nidra)

Place the body in an imaginary bed of sand, salt or healing clay. Relax the entire body. Extend tiny threadlike hairs from the back of the body into the earth. Start draining the body through the back. Let the feet go. Let the ankles go. The legs and thighs. Let the hips go. The vertebrae. The discs in between the vertebrae. The intestines: the large intestine, small intestine, the stomach, pancreas, liver and spleen. Let the kidneys relax, the lungs and heart. Let the rib cage unfold like a flower. Relax the shoulders, arms, wrists and hands. You don't need them anymore. Let the head fall into the sky. Relax the face and jaw. Heal the teeth, the roots of the teeth, the tongue, the gums. Heal the sinuses, the ears, the eyes. Let the eyes rest in the head. In your mind's eye, place the body under a waterfall of liquid light and let it wash the body clean. Thunderous pounding water from the Mother! Anything that was washed away left a space, fill that space with light. Float in the healing and absorb light as if through osmosis. Feel gratitude is it seeps into your skin... your cells... your bones... your joints... skull... Store the light in your bone marrow, rib cage, eyes, hands, wrists, fingernails, toenails, hair...

Place your body in a healing liquid. Become liquid yourself. Let the legs and feet swim. Let the arms go. The spine. The head. Visualize a healing nectar dripping from your bones down into your body. From the feet and knees, let the nectar drip into your legs. From the hands and wrists and elbows, let the nectar drip into your arms. Drops of nectar falling from the hips into the intestines, sex organs, bladder, liver, kidneys, stomach, pancreas, spleen. Drops of nectar falling from the top of your rib cage into your heart and lungs, down into your spine. Drops of nectar falling from your third eye into your brain, from your jaw into your neck, from your upper palette into your throat. Let the nectar drip down and heal the body. Let the eyes swim. Open into the sky of the mind. Let go. Unclench wherever you are clenching. Let go. Open into the sky of the mind. Graciously accept help and healing from the universe. Let the angels and deities heal you.

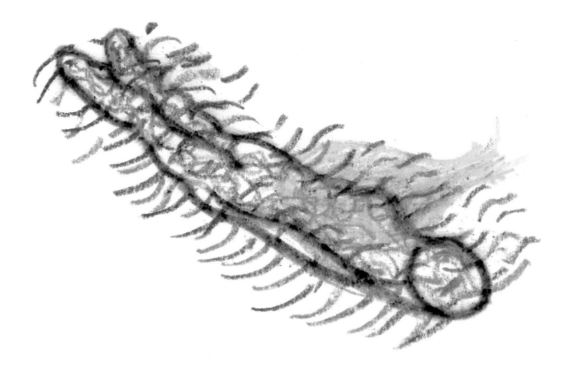

Place the body in a relaxed position, so you feel comfortable and undisturbed. Let the legs fall open slightly, let the breath come and go.... place yourself in a divine current - it could be the ocean, it could be a river, or tidepool. Let the body move freely with the current. Feel the salt water, or the minerals, or any healing substance (aloe vera, epsom salt, oils, aromas) seeping into the skin. The body is buoyant, you can breathe easily and freely.

Open the back body and let any worries or toxins drain out the back of the spine and head. Watch the toxins fall like sediment to the sandy bottom. See ash, minerals or dust falling away from the back body. Open the front of the body to divine light, like a flower opens to receive the sun. Open the rib cage like a lotus blossom, relax the pelvic bowl, open the skull as you would break open a piece of fruit. Let the divine nectar come peacefully into the front body, healing and nourishing the brain, spine, heart, lungs, kidneys, liver, stomach, pancreas, spleen, intestines, sexual organs, bladder. Get a divine suntan. Feel the sun on the face. Nourish the neck, shoulders and hips, moving the nectar outwards towards fingertips and toes. Absorb the nectar into every cell, drinking fully. Visualize your cells welcoming and absorbing the divine light through osmosis. Feel the transparency of every cell membrane as the nectar passes from outside to inside. Heal ears, eyes, nose, mouth, teeth, roots of the teeth, gums, tongue, hair... eyebrows, eyelids, eyelashes, forehead, cheeks... inner ear, middle ear, outer ear... sinuses, nose cartilage, brain matter, skullbone, scalp, hair, roots of the hair...

Rest for some time in the nectar of this divine current.

coming back from savasana

After healing in *savasana*, slowly bring your attention back to the body. Find the earth... Find your country... Find your city... this street... this room... In this room, one light is yours alone. One body has a vibration you recognize. In your mind's eye, bring your travel body three feet above your physical body. Don't do anything. Just hover. Float. Relax. Then draw your travel body into your physical body in one fell swoop through the navel point. Notice how spacious everything is on the inside. Rearrange some furniture. Add some color. Change what's on the walls. Redesign the place. Let the healing energy flow. Move the fingers and toes very slowly like reeds in the wind. Slowly. Check the connections between your brain and your feet. The signals criss-cross at the navel. Rotate the ankles and wrists. Take a deep breath in and stretch the arms up overhead. Stretch the feet away from the hands. Stretch! Open the mouth wide and breathe out. Close the mouth. Rub the palms together and place palms over the eyes. Open the eyes into the hands. See how connected your eyes and your hands are now. Rub the palms together again and move the palms over your face, neck and hair, like you were washing your face with an imaginary healing water. Run your fingers through your hair, press your fingertips into your scalp and massage the head. You can also grab tufts of hair and move the hair back and forth so the scalp moves over the skullbone. Place the arms on the floor out to the sides like you are on a cross. Bend one knee up to the chest, tuck the toes under the opposite knee and twist the spine. Keep the shoulder blades on the floor. Do the other side. Then bring your knees to your chest and rock on the spine from your shoulders to your tailbone, don't forget the vertebrae at the waist. Come sitting up in a comfortable position and let the energy settle.

Using the magnetism of your spirit, draw your bones, muscles and ligaments back into place. Watch as your spirit pulls the blood vessels, nerve tissue, and lymphatic system into natural alignment. Only pull back that which is dear to you... Only build the body with light... beautiful, fresh, vibrant living parts. Pull them into your system and relish their form...

Find a clear, thin coating of light and wrap it around the body like skin - translucent, reflecting and holding light, protecting the body, and clear enough that people can see you through it. Paint the skin, hair and nails with light - the eyelashes, eyebrows, the skin color, eyes, and hair. Be creative, use color. You may paint in several shades of the same color...

Slowly move the fingers and toes, checking the connections. Your right fingers connect to the left brain, your left toes connect to the right brain. Rotate the wrists and ankles... Rub the palms together, stretch the arms overhead and take a deep breath in, stretching the toes away from the hands. Open the mouth wide. Rub the palms together, and splash the face and neck with the energy in the hands. Bend the knees to the chest, rock on the spine from the tailbone to the shoulder blades or neck for 30 seconds. Come sitting up in a comfortable position. Join the fingertips and thumbtips together in front of the solar plexus, creating a beautiful vibrant energy between your palms. This energy is for you alone. Then press the palms together and internalize the healing energy. Bow the head to the heart. *Namaste*.

When I wake up, if I wake up
When I wake up I will try to remember The Dream...
You know, it's always there if I close my eyes
I can feel the warmth of the sun. It's always there
Somewhere in the world there is always a light on.

But it doesn't last more than an hour maybe half a day
Everything changes before I know which way to go, what way to turn.
It doesn't last even though I try to find a way.
Everything changes before I know which way to go, what way to turn.
When I wake up, when I wake up
When I wake up I will try to remember The Dream...

meditation

Buildings hold energy. The beams, walls, and flooring retain the vibrations of what has been experienced within it. Your bones and musculature provide structure for your body; they also retain the vibrations of what has been experienced by you. In the same way that architecture shapes your environment, *mudras* and *asanas* direct the energy within the body. The feng shui of a building is affected by its entryways, inner flow, and exits. The body is also affected by energy coming in, circulating, and releasing. I practice meditation as good feng shui - I place the body in a healing posture, seal off the outside world and its stimuli, and sit in silence.

The first step in meditation is sealing off the outside world. You get way more information each day than you actually need. The wisdom of the soul is placed within. To access it, you need quiet. You can use your breath to create a space of silence for meditation. Closing the throat slightly to create a whisper sound in the throat *(ujjayi pranayama)* will slow down your breathing pattern. Measure your inhale and exhale and then extend it (if you counted to 4, gradually lengthen it to 6 or 12). You can attach a mantra to your inhale (*Ma*) and exhale (*Om*). Visualization can enhance your experience; you can visualize beautiful energy coming in on the inhale and integrating into the body on the exhale. Create a closed circuit of energy with the breath. Don't let the energy escape on the exhale; visualize a continuous flow of energy and breath which heals and nourishes. Think of it like osmosis; you don't need to get rid of your old energy, it will simply float off your skin. An exchange of spirit through a translucent base membrane.

Once your energy is sealed off from the outside world, you can focus on enhancing your inner world. Visualization and *mantras* can create a beautiful energy within. I think of it as an intravenous bliss drip. Divine dialysis. As you assume your meditation posture and slow down your breathing, mind and body slow their rhythms and rebalance. Your energy recharges, you become more you, your thoughts become more clear. In this silence, you can speak with your guides, your angels, yourself. Keep the *mantra* and breath awareness going, keep the posture, and notice the dialogue.

The best time for meditation is before sunrise - there are less earthly activities, less media broadcasts, less interference. I include meditation at the end of yoga class because I feel it is a good way to integrate the healing energy in body, mind and spirit. It's important to take a moment at the end of yoga class to settle and integrate the energy into your bones, muscles, brain tissue, heart, lungs, spirit... Come into a meditative posture, hold a *mudra*, close the eyes, slow the breath. If you are leaning forward, lean back a little bit. Soften. Let the energy recycle and do its work.

meditation

Shri Shivabalayogi meditated for 23 hours a day for eight years and 12 hours a day for four years to complete a rigorous spiritual discipline called *tapasya*. (www.shiva.org) He gives these two simple commands for meditation:

1 - Keep the eyes still. *(The eyes are still.)*
2 - Keep the body still. *(You lose sensation of the body.)*

So when you meditate, find a comfortable position to sit in and stay there. Keep the eyes closed and relaxed. If you are meditating for a set amount of time, use a timer so you don't have to look at the clock.

For short periods of meditation (1-10 minutes), I form *mudras* with my hands and close the eyes down til they are barely open. The eyes are rolled upwards into the head, either focusing at the third eye point (at the forehead where the eyebrows meet) or at the top of the head. Some teachers describe the eyelids as 9/10ths closed. It's a very small amount; any more than that will sever your connection to the mind screen. When your eyes are partially closed in this way, you will see the mind screen and a small window of reality at the same time. If your hands are in a *mudra* or in your lap, you will barely see your hands at the same time as you view the mind screen. For long periods of meditation, I interlace my fingers or relax my hands in my lap and close my eyes down completely.

It is a good idea to cover the spine with a shawl or blanket. Sitting on a cushion or bolster will help your posture as well as ground your energy. Focusing the mind on *mantra*, breath or visualizations will help you stay connected to spirit and avoid the mind chatter. These visualizations are done with eyes closed and are coordinated with the breath. Bring white light in through the top of the head and carefully follow the light coming down through each chakra. Deep violet in the center of the skull, azure blue in the center of the throat, spring green at the heart, yellow at the navel, orange at the belly, and red at the base of the spine. Inhale and exhale at each *chakra*, visualizing the color and texture of the energy. My favorite visualization technique is inhaling and drawing energy from the top of the head down to the heart, exhaling and letting the energy settle, moving from the heart down to the base of the spine. The energy often ignites at the bottom, becoming white energy once again and feeding the aura.

Slow the breath. Hold the body still. Hold the eyes still. Pray with a melting heart. The teachings will arise out of the silence.

> *Think of your spine as a connective pathway between heaven and earth. Heaven moves down through the top of the spine and earth moves up from the bottom. Your body is where it all integrates. Your ability to mix spirit and flesh will determine how well connected you feel in your life.*

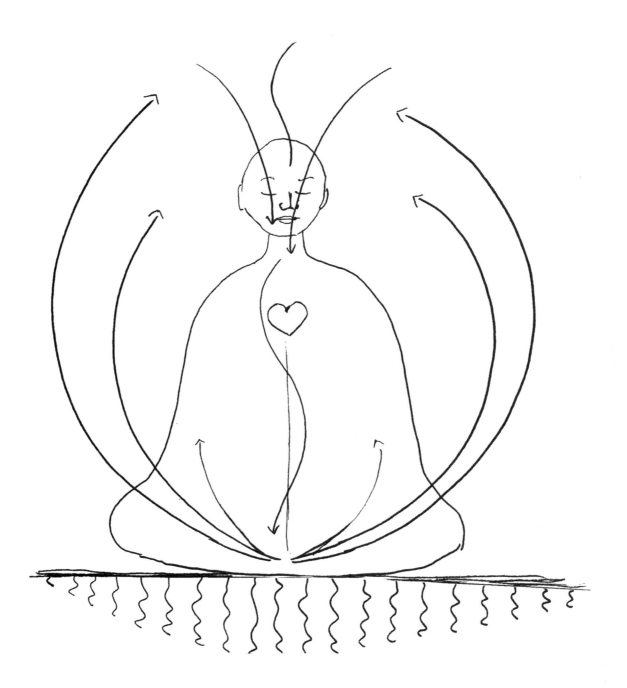

mudras

wisdom gesture *(Gyan Mudra)* - press first finger and thumbtip together on each hand. This is an effective and simple way to create internal awareness.

interlaced fingers *(Venus Mudra)* - interlace fingers and place in lap. This is a great mudra to feel cozy and grounded. You can visualize energy falling from heaven, collecting in the hands and base of the spine.

recirculating gesture - create *gyan mudra* on each hand, rest the right hand in the left and join the backs of the Jupiter fingers. Hold this mudra at the solar plexus, a few inches away from the body. Solar plexus is the seat of change, so this mudra recycles the energy of change back into the body.

quiet gesture - join Sun finger (ring finger) and thumbtip on one hand and Saturn finger (middle ringer) and thumbtip on the other hand.

lotus blossom mudra - joining Sun fingers (ring fingers), thumbs and insides of the wrists, hold this mudra at the heart. In your minds eye, visualize your fingers extending for many miles, and then draw energy into the space between the hands. This looks like a lotus blossom held at the heart; you can visualize it internally as well.

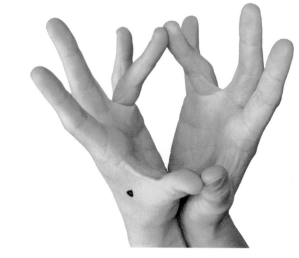

supreme source mudra *(Mahayoni Mudra)*
classical - interlace Sun (ring fingers) and Mercury (pinky) fingers, touch Saturn (middle) fingertips together, Jupiter (first finger) wraps around the back, thumbtips touch. You can hold hands at heart center or let them rest in the lap.

easier variation - backwards interlace the fingers, bringing fingertips together. Join Jupiter fingers and thumbtips.

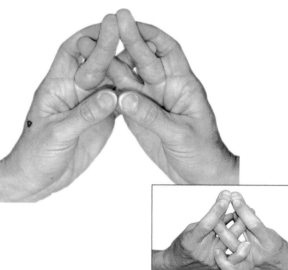

mudras

Mudra translates as 'seal.' Mudras are used to seal off the energy from the outside world. They create closed circuits by binding the extremities (hands, feet, base of spine, eyes, and tongue) so the energy recycles back into the body. This creates a cozy internal space for you to meditate in and increases the spiritual intensity of your practice.

wrist strengthening

How much weight should you put in your hands? As much as feels comfortable. Gentle, consistent strengthening gives the best results.

no weight - Standing up, place your hand on a wall at the same level as your shoulder, fingers pointing back. Your shoulderblade will naturally pull into alignment, palm (suction) the wall, turn your feet 45° away from wall and stretch.

a little weight - From all 4s, lean back onto your knees and take the weight off your hands. Palm the ground and lift the heels of the hands up off the floor.

some weight - From all 4s, put weight on the hands, suction the palms, press the fingertips into the ground and lift the heels of the hands up. Press up through your first two fingers so you don't sickle the wrist.

full weight - From platform (or even handstand), lift the heels of the hands. Wow, just thinking about it makes me hug the midline...

With your hands, pull the energy from the ground into your heart. Like a plant, use the root-like structure of your fingers to draw nourishment from the earth.

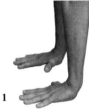 1   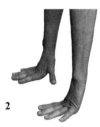 2   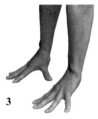 3

I use these hand positions to develop strength in the wrists and hands. They can be used in downward dog, *vinyasa*, or any pose which bears weight directly on the hands.

1 palms flat - Spread your fingers like the rays of the sun, thumbs pointing towards each other. Suction the palm against the floor as if you were palming a basketball. Then press the tips of the fingers into the floor.

2 mounds of fingers - Lift the heels of your hands off the floor, keeping the elbows straight. Center the weight between the 1st and 2nd knuckles of the hand so you don't sickle the wrist. Draw the forearms towards each other and hug the midline. This strengthens the wrists and forearms.

3 fingertips - Come up onto the fingertips, distributing the weight evenly on all ten fingertips. This develops suction power in the palms.

The Anusara Yoga principles of alignment can be applied to any style of yoga (www.anusara.com)

hug the muscles to the bone - Squeeze your muscles towards your bones and activate muscular energy. Create a flow of energy from the extremities into the body core. Muscular energy is balanced by organic energy (shining out through the pose).

hug the midline - Pull muscles together towards the center of the body. Left and right will pull to center (as in prayer pose) or front and back will pull to center (as in front lunge when the legs pull towards each other).

melting the heart - Lifting the shoulders slightly as you round the shoulders back allows the shoulder blades to pull together. This gives strength to any pose which bears weight on the arms. Melting the heart is balanced by puffing the kidneys.

inner spiral - When you spiral the thighs inwards, the sit bones widen and allow you to deepen your standing poses. Inner spiral is balanced by the tailbone dropping down.

What you are doing now is the
most important moment of your life.

THE
ROLES
WE
PLAY

self-examination

your vehicle: the body

The body is a vehicle for you. It's not actually who you are. It gives you a way to experience your life. In yogic scripture, the physical body is looked at as a great blessing, earned from many lifetimes of devotion.

A human incarnation is the most desirable of all the incarnations. Why? The human incarnation has the capacity for transformation. Spiritual consciousness, superconsciousness, is unique to human beings. Other incarnations experience and absorb knowledge, but few have the capacity for inner growth. You as a human have the capacity to remember previous incarnations. Your remembrance of being a tree - powerful, majestic, patient. Your remembrance of being a dolphin - superintelligent, expansive, free. Your remembrance of being a rat - diligent, relentless, hoarding. You may remember other human incarnations as well. The Dalai Lama says 'We are all one.' In a yogic perspective, his words are literal. We actually are one. After a certain number of reincarnations, we converge on a similar reality. We have all experienced the same incarnations. Our understanding widens. We know the many facets of human existence. Understanding all living things because we have been there. We are all part of the same thing. Even the physical makeup of our bodies mirrors the minerals and water of all other creation.

So the body is your vital and integral link to your experiences here on earth. It is the vehicle through which you experience your life. Through the body you taste juicy strawberries. Through the body you enjoy surfing at the beach. Through the body you smell the soup cooking, experience lovemaking, raise children. All karmas have to be experienced through the physical body - there is no other way.

Karma means *action* or *doing*. Karmas are the things we do. Sometimes karmas are seen as the things we are compelled to do. What we do with our lives is of utmost importance. Every action has effect. The events of our lives are our classroom.

It is only on earth in a physical body that karmas can be worked through. You can't meditate them away. You can't sit in your meditation and say, 'And now I will experience love.' You have to fall in love with someone. Be swept off your feet. Head over heels. When you fall in love, you find yourself doing the things that lovers do. When someone else describes falling in love, you know exactly what they are talking about because you've experienced it. If you hadn't experienced it yourself, you wouldn't really know.

Each karma is specific and meaningful. You are put in a situation which will bring out various aspects of the human condition. I call these situations ROLES. You adopt certain roles to fulfill certain changes. All this activity combined is called *karma*.

The role that you play will only last a certain amount of time. Nothing goes on forever. You might be a yoga teacher now; later on, you will become a mother. Whatever you think you are, will change in a year or ten year's time.

Some people so deeply identify with the role they are playing, the role becomes their whole identity. For example, if you think you are Sally's husband and the big family man on the block, when the relationship crumbles, part of you crumbles with it. We all think we are who we think we are. It's only natural.

What you are doing is playing a ROLE. You take on certain roles in your life to affect certain changes in your heart. As your roles change, it might look like your life is "falling apart," when actually you are just moving into a new karmic fulfillment. The illusion is in thinking that you are what you do or as others perceive you. You are you; there is something that remains constant throughout all those changes. There is a part of you that is the same as when you were a child, that will be the same after you are dead. There is part of you that is the same in this incarnation as it was in the last incarnation. Your body changes, your incarnation changes, you relationships change; but some part of you doesn't change. Some call it soul or Self.

Self-awareness is one of the keys to enlightenment. But becoming aware of the Self (the part of you that doesn't change) is not so easy. We can access the Self partly through yoga, meditation and chanting; but introspection is also necessary.

Unresolved issues are stored in the physical body. If a desire is in you, but never experienced, it will linger. Some part of the soul retains this desire and carries it to the next life. The only way to process our issues is through experience - learning, failing, studying and trying again. Desires show you what you are interested in working on and shed light on the areas you wish to explore.

Rasa is a Sanskrit word for bliss. It is a tangible nectar, a juice, a by-product of spiritual practice. *Rasa* can be stored in the energetic lines of the body. It can be stored in muscle tissue, nerves, cells. In the same way that architecture holds energy, your physical body stores and holds energy. Not just in your bones, muscles, organs, bone marrow, blood cells and skin, but also in your electromagnetic field. Healers can use this stored energy to heal, transmitting *rasa* to others. The abundance of light particles makes saints, *sadhus* and healers attractive. They have light to share. The transmission of light is a part of the work of many saints and healers.

I am going to ask you to view your life from a different vantage point. Not from your mind, but from the place you functioned from before you took incarnation. When you were searching for a body, you interviewed all the possible prospects and chose the best, most appropriate set of parents for you. How did you make that decision? Did you use your brain? Impossible, you didn't have a brain, you didn't even have a body yet. And yet you made a decision. How did you arrive at that decision? Wherever you were functioning from then, I want you to function from now.

Many people have an overview of themselves at the time of death or near death. People claim it is as if they are hovering over their body, watching it and all the surrounding circumstances. At the moment of death, all the memories of the life are brought before the mind in rapid succession (just like we did in this meditation), superfast, a million memories per minute. And you decide, how did I do? Did I accomplish what I meant to accomplish? Hmmm, didn't handle that one very well... I did OK over here... I was mean to my mother... I neglected my husband... and so on. Why not get that overview now, why wait until death?

Some describe their most profound meditative moment being an experience of the universe being one, all things pulsating with the same energy, all plants, people, animals, and atoms being undeniably interconnected. All beings having the same composition, the same atomic and cellular makeup, all beings created from the same chemicals and electrical impulses. In fact, many healers, visionaries and psychics claim that the information they receive is simply brought to them "on the wind", that it is all contained in the elemental nature of living beings. The sound of creation itself (OM) is said to contain all knowledge, individual and collective.

The Dalai Lama has said we are all one. This is not a metaphor. It's a practical statement. Each of us plays certain roles during our life. When we all have played all of those roles, then we can truly feel that we are one with everyone.

Each role has the potential to change us in some way. The role is a catalyst to invigorate a certain aspect of who we are. The role you play is not you; it is not the essence of your spirit. It is one aspect of who you are. By playing the role, you uncover certain energies within you. The roles are temporary. Who you are inside is permanent. The roles come and go. The changes they affect inside you are lasting.

All of our *karmas*, our experiences, have to be experienced fully and completely. They cannot be thought about, meditated through, or experienced vicariously. You have to go through the experience to know it. Anyone else who has gone through it will know exactly what you are talking about when you describe it. You will have a shared experience, an empathy with that person. When you have empathy for all beings, you have experienced what the Dalai Lama describes as being one.

roles

How many roles have you experienced? Here are a few possible roles:

The Aggressor	*The Recluse*	*The Recluse*	*The Student*
The Hero	*The Helper*	*The Provider*	*The Teacher*
The Fool	*The Rescuer*	*The Victim*	*The Beggar*
The Lover	*The Diplomat*	*The Caregiver*	*The One Being Cared For*
The Abused One	*The Reviled One*	*The Protector*	*The Celebrated, Famous One*
The Invisible One	*The Survivor*	*The Successful One*	*The Mother/Father/Parent*

Sit in a comfortable position. Slow down the breath. Close your eyes and relax into Oneness. I am going to take you back in time to the time before this life when you were still deciding which body to take... Find yourself as a floating soul... watch yourself enter your mother's womb... witness your birth... remember scenes from your childhood, where you lived, where you played... see yourself getting your first job... your first romances... experience a great moment in your life, an achievement... watch yourself progressing along your life path... becoming older, learning, growing...

meditation

Continue until you come to present time... see yourself as you are now... where you currently live... your relationships... your job... and now progress into the future... see the next place you will live... the transitions of parents and loved ones... see yourself in ten years... just feel the possibility, it doesn't have to be specific... continue through time and find yourself in later years peaceful enjoying life, and progressing to your final days before death. Watch yourself leaving your physical body... floating like mist, up and away, the pull of spirit being so irresistible... moving back into Oneness.

Stay with the breath as you slowly bring your consciousness back to the present moment. Open the eyes without focusing them and close them. Do this a few times until you are accustomed to the light and your surroundings. Take a deep breath in, stretch the arms or body and relax with eyes open.

exploration

Now that you have viewed your life from a distance, let's write down two chapters of that life, including some details associated with each one (a person's name, a place, the name of the company you worked for, the address of your old house). Next to each situation, write down what you got out of it. Why did you select this situation for yourself? What did you learn?

Now find the section of your life that completed before you started this one. Take the role you recently completed and write down how it affected you, how it changed you, what things you learned, what became stronger through playing that role. It doesn't matter what you write down, even a few words, whatever comes to mind. This is something you have now mastered. A chapter of life which is completed. Give it a name. Write down why you did this chapter. What did you get out of it?

And now look at your current work, your current situation. Write down a few details associated with it. Next to it, write down what the end result of all this work will be. How will you feel once you have accomplished this work, completed this chapter?

Now we're going to work in partners. (If you are reading this book, or wish to work alone, continue in solitary fashion.) With a partner, describe what's bugging you about what you're current role. What are you working on? What or who really bugs you? Answer this question, "What really bugs me about my current situation is...." Have your partner write down what you just said. Now have your partner write you an affirmation based on the opposite of what you just said. Retain the positive and turn around the negative. If you said, "I'm silly, distracted and playful and I hate fighting with my wife," your partner would write, "I am focused and playful and find insight in my relationship." It's just for fun. Don't take it as the end-all truth. We're just exploring. Have your partner write down what role he or she thinks you are playing. Have them hand the paper back to you. You now have three pieces

of information: your role, the end result of playing that role, and your affirmation to get there.

Then switch partners. It's your turn to listen now and write down their frustrations and difficulties with their current life work. Write down what role you think he or she is playing. Hand the paper back to them. Discuss for a moment, if this information "fits." Did your partner describe you accurately? Change a few words if you need to, so that it does fit.

It's important to do the "end result" directly after meditation, while you still have an overview of your life. Then break into partners and talk about current events. Talking to a partner about current life situations is often more revealing than solitary contemplation. Another person's perspective on your life role can be helpful.

In defining the role, be aware that it is not about how it looks. It is only about how it feels. You can see in the past how previous roles benefitted you. Can you look ahead in the future and see what this will do for you in the end? Will it strengthen you? Soften you? Give you knowledge? Give you humility? How will you be changed by playing this role? Your previous role is very comfortable to you. This is now something that you have mastered. It's a favorite role, it comes easily. You will often adopt this favored role with your new situation. If you were a victim in your last relationship, you might adopt the role of victim in a new relationship even with a nonabusive partner. If you were a caregiver, you might adopt the role of caregiver with someone who is perfectly capable.

But now you're in a new role. That old role is no longer necessary. You are being asked to work on something different. Your new role will be your weak link. It is an aspect of you which is hidden or underdeveloped. It feels awkward. In fact, if you were given the choice, you would probably choose a different role altogether. You don't want to play the role of Empathic Caregiver, but there it is. It's on your plate; your life circumstances are asking you to play this role. Remember, you do not choose your role from an emotional point of view or by using your brain. You choose a role from a soul perspective, as a pathway to help yourself grow. It will take time to develop new skills to fulfill your new role.

Many of us are surprised by the roles we adopt. The roles can feel uncomfortable, unusual, not what we expected. Sometimes we find ourselves doing something very different than we thought we would or should be doing. Life turned out differently than we expected. We were asked to play roles we didn't think we would ever adopt.

The advice we give to others we can give to ourselves. "You know, what you really should do is..." "What would be REALLY good for you is this..." We do it naturally, in an effort to guide and support the people we care about. How would you do this for yourself? If I think of my own life, I can only conclude that if I had to watch over me, I would *definitely* have put me in an ashram. Can you imagine, a precocious teenager with some psychic skills, good looks, and a sharp mind... I was arrogant, superior, and disappointed with the world. What I wanted more than anything was some spiritual training, a hardcore bootcamp to give me the basics of spiritual knowledge and discipline. So I adopted the role of STUDENT. I went on to play LEADER, LOVER and PARENT.

To determine the role, ask, "What is life asking of me right now? What things am I currently doing?"

To get your affirmation, complete this sentence, "What really bugs me about my current situation is..." Take the words you use to describe your current issues and use the opposite to create a positive affirmation.

To find the end result, ask, "What will change as a result of my playing this role? How will I feel once I have mastered it? When it's all behind me, how will I feel?

Alan was a hard working executive (PROVIDER) on Wall Street who became very successful (THE SUCCESSFUL ONE). He then fell in love (LOVER) and had 7 years of wonderful marriage. Through his love relationship, he was able to soften his approach to life and relinquish his hold on the alcoholism which developed during his career. His role became STUDENT. A desire for deeper learning, for spiritual knowledge arose in him, and he started taking some courses. He did so tentatively at first, just a class here or there. This developed into extensive teacher trainings with various spiritual teachers. He can see that the end result of taking on this role is a deep inner joy. He describes his role as JOY SEEKER. "I am a happy student who finds inner joy."

* * * * * * * *

"She gave me the finger! Can you believe that?!" says one. Other people in the workshop just shrug. "So? What's the big deal?" The pain in her voice is present because she is activating new energies. They're called growth pains. What bothers one person will not bother another person at all. Each person will be irritated by something different. It reflects the work being done. The work you have to do is expertly tailored to you.

How a role looks from the outside is very often not what it feels like from the inside. You may see a successful businessman and feel he is playing the SUCCESSFUL ONE role. But in fact, that role is behind him (you see the residues of his mastery of this previous role). He is now in the role of LOVER and it is totally messing him up. He's turned inside out, topsy turvy, trying to figure out his heart. The role is how it feels from the inside, not what it looks like from the outside.

The role is a trigger. It is not you. The person in front of you is not real either. They are playing a specific part for your benefit. They are creating the trigger for you. It is important to remember, because the person you are mad at is just playing a role. You can experience total love and still have an amazing terrible fight, screaming at the top of your lungs, fully aware that it is "the stuff" working out. No harm to each person.

Opening to a new role can be difficult. The last role we played we mastered. It now comes easily to us. It is part of our identity. Take the MOTHER who is now an EXECUTIVE, washing people's coffee mugs at work. It's ingrained. It was not so ingrained when she first became a mother. It felt peculiar, providing every morsel of food and being called upon every minute of the day for what the child needed. Now every minute of the day is naturally attuned to helping others. Her new role as EXECUTIVE requires that she develop leadership qualities. These will activate slowly, and it may even feel painful to leave the qualities of nurturing behind.

There is nothing permanent, you are in constant conversation with your life all the time. Everything is in constant change, your cells change, your environment changes. If you saw all the lives at once it would look like NYC at rush hour. But that's because you're looking from the outside. Every person in that seeming chaos is going in a specific direction. Your body is the same way; every ligament knows its purpose, every bloodcell knows exactly where its going. It's the same with you. You understand your karma. You actually know what you are doing, deep down. It's nothing you can't figure out. It's an intuition, it's a soul thing, a spirit thing. You know it because you designed it before you even had this body.

You have to be loved, appreciated, betrayed, tricked, cheated, nurtured, saved... the list is endless. As many human experiences as there are, that's what you have to experience. You see a young kid trying to figure out how to tie his shoelaces. He's getting frustrated. You were there once. You see a young parent caring for his or her child. You yourself are starting a family. You watch to see how they are dealing with their child. Later on, you might pass a grandparent on the sidewalk. Her hair is white, she's smiling, but she's in her own world. She barely notices you. You will be there someday. The cosmos is one. We will do it all and experience it all by the end. It may take many lifetimes.

Some people feel fearful or trapped by the role they have currently adopted, thinking it will last the rest of their life. I say to them, Relax! Just like all the other chapters, this one too will come to an end. Celebrate the advent of your new role. If you are to be alone, make it fun. Pretend you are on sabbatical. Plan enriching activities. Decorate your solitary cave. Or if you are just beginning your role as Provider, create rewards for yourself after making a certain amount of money. Break it down into rewardable, manageable chunks of time. And know that this role, too, will not last forever. But it is the perfect thing for you right now. And it's the only way into the future of who you will become.

what
are
you
doing?

My previous role was THE SUPPORTER. I always did things behind the scenes, never taking credit or attracting attention. For three years, I worked as manager to a recording artist. I was given the opportunity to work on myself in solitude. I was then led into the role of TEACHER. Not wanting to take credit for anything made it difficult to be an authority. It was clear to me that my job as teacher was to create a heart centered space for everyone, but I had trouble asking for what I needed after being the Supporter. I didn't want to take a stand on anything for fear of hurting people's feelings. "I fearlessly hold heartspace for myself and others, so we all can experience a higher state of consciousness." The affirmations are simple, but each role is difficult because it activates an energy that wasn't there before.

*   *   *   *   *   *   *   *

Dale is in the role of STUDENT; his "end result" is an experience of inner joy. This is his affirmation, his intention, his guide. In finding teachers and learning from different masters, difficulties come up. This isn't what he planned for, or this teacher isn't quite right, etc. Should he stay with this teacher or find another? Should he study with many teachers or just one? He uses the end result as a guide. If the training develops an awareness of inner joy, he sticks with it. One course more or less will not change the overall pattern. Even if the teacher is morally corrupt, Dale will still be able to gain the information and techniques he needs to continue his journey towards inner joy.

Each role is valuable to us, and should not be discredited. Do not discredit having played the role of THE ABUSED ONE. It strengthened you, started your martial arts training, developed your compassion for other abused victims, initiated your role into LEADERSHIP to help others. Do not discredit having played the role of THE SUCCESSFUL ONE. It gave you self-esteem, showed you the bounty of God's creation. When you went bankrupt and played the role of BEGGAR, you figured out how to crawl out of that hole and it developed an unshakable self-trust. No one can touch that or take it away.

The role is like a piece of clothing. It is worn for a period of time and then dropped. The role is not permanent. The only thing that is permanent is what you got out of it. How were you changed? What inner changes happened as a result of this role? Being FAMOUS is just a role. Next year you may not be FAMOUS. You may be RECLUSE. What inner changes did being famous create? In the end, it is only the inner changes you walk away with.

The role is something you adopt. It feels strange at first, it develops areas that are weak in you. As you integrate into the role and its work, you become more familiar with it. You master it. You work through the karmas associated with that situation. When the karmas are burned up, you're done. The role is dropped. You move on to the next role.

While some roles that last only a short time are life changing, most of us focus our attention on roles of longer duration. The roles which last for months or years, which place us in certain situations and create opportunities for inner work.

don't sweat the details

"I listen to people's problems all day long. They don't really want to change, they just want someone to talk to, someone who shows they care. They talk and I listen and then they change (or don't change) according to the way they already are." She's a psychiatrist, but she no longer enjoys it. She's bored and exasperated. I ask her what programs she creates for her patients. She describes a few things. I ask her if she does these same helpful programs for herself She laughs and says no. Her role as LISTENER/PSYCHIATRIST is over. She's done with it. You can hear it in her voice. She's gotten all she needs to get out of that role. What will she do next? I don't know... does it matter? Do we need to know everything? Your heart will guide you to the next step.

Karmas are horizontal energy. They are interactions between people, changes in circumstance, comparisons, judgments, kindness or lending a helping hand. Karmas are how we are connected to each other. Vertical communication is your connection to spirit. You need vertical connection to master spiritual and psychic planes.

It's not up to you to plan your life. You did that before you took incarnation. What you have to do now is align with your intended work for this lifetime. If you sit quietly, you will find your intention. Write it down, state it clearly before your practice, state it clearly to end your practice. Start a conversation with the Universe. And then begin your activity. It's not up to you to work out the details; your life work can be done in any number of possible settings. It's a creative, playful work (God's play), so let Him enjoy a little. The way in which the Universe manifests opportunities for you is Its way of responding to your queries. Don't worry if this is the right choice for you. Whatever it is that you are doing, apply yourself 100% to it – caring for your sick mother, working for an ad agency, teaching elementary school. Do it with kindness. The inner work is contained within the circumstance you have been given.

Keep your focus inwards. Your work is unique. Try not to compare yourself to those around you - friends, family, colleagues.. Comparing your role to someone else's is pointless. Their karma is totally different from yours. Even though you may be in the same role as someone else, what you are getting out of it is totally different. Comparison is a mental distraction which limits your connection to yourself and the Universe. Listen to your guides, your guiding forces. If things are not going right, direct your questions to them. Do your work and don't look around too much. Keep your connection vertical, and don't stray into horizontal detours.

keep a vertical connection

Mary is in the role of LOVER. All day long she thinks about her lover, in fact she doesn't do much else. She buys him gifts, meets him at the airport, they take walks together, laugh and spend hours and hours hanging out. Is this OK? Shouldn't she be getting down to work eventually? Not really. The role of LOVER gives her a chance to feel nourished, comforted, appreciated, pampered. It gives her soul a chance to play. Her last role was as the Provider, so she feels frivolous and silly. But the role of Lover will develop a deep trust in herself and in the Universe. She will taste human kindness and the sweetness possible in this world. She will come to understand that she can manifest beauty, grace and peace in her life and share it with others.

We have these ways of holding ourselves and we can't get rid of it. I call it a layer of polyurethane (shellac for you Brits out there). A clear coating surrounds your true Self. You can see who you are and your friends can see who you are, but you can't touch it and they can't touch it. Even though you intellectually understand it all, you can't come out and be who you really are. A teacher will do everything possible to shatter that layer of illusion. Scrambling your brain, asking you to do the impossible, performing the miraculous are all tried and true methods used by the saints.

Sometimes your life is the teacher. When your life takes the unexpected twist, that's when everything unravels and you can look at yourself as if for the first time.

A spiritual teacher will put you in situations which you have no skills for. Why? It's their job. They have to bring out the underdeveloped areas, the hidden aspects of your personality. They look for the weakness. Not because they are critical, but because they love you. They watch you, what your reaction is to everything. Pretend your guru says, "I think you should go to India." and you think, "Hmm... India... that'll be amazing, get away from America, sink into the culture there... cool" The reaction is smooth. So then your guru says, "Actually, I've changed my mind. You should stay in America and work at the bookstore with Sheila." "SHEILA?!" you think, "She's a jerk! I'm definitely NOT going to work with Sheila. She's crazy. It's like PMS every other day with that woman." Your mind explodes with a reaction. Your Guru says, "Very good. Stay in America and work with Sheila."

Amma gave one command to a devotee: Smile. This was not the devotee's normal tendency; in fact, this devotee was often depressed. It took enormous energy for her to smile at people on the street. She felt foolish. It seemed fake, and utterly ridiculous. A waste of time. Why bother? A smile? Oh please! But as she progressed, she found it activated joy both in her and the people around her. It activated new energy in a positive direction.

polyurethane

Fear is part of having an incarnation. If you have a body, you have fear. No fear, no incarnation.

-Shri Shivabalayogi

am I done yet?

When your work in the role is complete, the external circumstances dissolve. The kids move out, you downsize the house. Suddenly you are finished with the role of MOTHER. The role is simply no longer there. How do you know when it's over? The Universe tells you. The external circumstances are manifestations for our inner work. When the inner work is done, the external environment changes. Don't try to change your external world, do your internal work and the external will shift all by itself.

There's a difference between pain and adjustment. When something hurts, you respond by changing your alignment, or taking your hand off the stove. Adjustment is different than pain. If you hold your arm up in a yoga exercise, it becomes annoying, but it isn't pain. It's an adjustment. Making adjustments in your life can be aggravating as well. There is some necessary discomfort as you change or grow into a new role.

Change requires effort. An enormous amount of energy is required to make even the smallest change in your heart. In yoga, you have to exert double effort to try a new pose. To get beyond what you know takes great energy and enthusiasm. Keep trying! Every time you walk down that new path, you create an energy which you can build on next time. After awhile, your body retains the information and it becomes second nature.

Sometimes, when the work is deep, the discomfort is also deep. You might not want to continue living. Or you might say you can't bear to stay in this relationship. You have to sit in the situation and allow it to do its work on you. If you run away, without resolving the issue, it will crop up somewhere else later on. Most people do not know how to sit in uncomfortable situations and grow. That is why meditation is so good - you have to continue sitting for the prescribed time, no matter what mental state you are in. Don't pray to get out of your situation, pray for the strength to be in it.

How do you know when to quit the role? Well, you never really do quit. It simply ends on its own. One day you change, it changes. You keep looking for the signs, some indication that it's over. If you quit too soon, that same role will reappear so you can complete the work. If you haven't changed your heart, you'll continue working on the same issue with different people.

signs along the way

If you are meditative, you may get the indications of change prior to their actually happening in real time. Meditators, healers, and psychics often have dreams, visions, or messages about things before they happen. If you are in tune with this, you will receive the signals of change days, months, even many months before they actually happen. But visions and knowledge don't change the work at hand. Your work is in the present.

Even so, you might need reassurance that you are in the right place, doing the right thing. When you plan out your life, you create some key situations which, when you experience them, will reassure you that you are on the right path. Certain roles can appear like signposts along the way. I experience it as a kind of deja vu. Those sensations appear to me as a sign of fulfillment for this lifetime. It is not a remembrance of something that happened before, but rather an acknowledgment that I am actually doing what I planned to do.

I had one of these feelings while doing a CD with a music producer named Herb. We had been working 50 hours a week for several months, creating special arrangements, sound effects, agonizing over each track, scrutinizing the feel of each song, etc. On this particular day, I was recording in a separate room and Herb and I were communicating via microphones and headphones. Herb was coaching me on my vocals as we recorded the final tracks. He said to me, "OK look...It's just like a video, you can see every piece of the story as it unfolds. Take your time, you can do this. OK, here we go... make it hot." The sensation was unmistakable. I felt an eerie out-of-body, looking-down-on-myself feeling. I realized then that this very experience, these words that Herb said to me, was something I knew I would experience if I stuck it out over the long term with the project. If I had quit (which I wanted to do 2 or 3 times over the course of the year I worked with him) I would not have experienced the growth, refinement of spirit, and strength of human conviction which I ended up experiencing by the end of the project. When we were doing the final vocals (10 months and $40,000 into the project) I finally experienced this deja vu. It confirmed to me that I had made the right decision by sticking it out. This role was vital to my spirit evolving. Risking our life savings on this project was part of my growth. It helped me when I got confirmation on a soul level because it sure hadn't made any sense business-wise.

Sometimes I can see the role I am in, what it will do for me and where it will lead. So I get impatient. Only halfway through the process (say, a year and a half into it), I'll say, "OK, I'm done! I get it. Next role please..." But in reality, I've only skimmed the surface of its effects. It takes time to understand the subtleties of each role and experience it fully.

When I was touring and managing a certain recording artist, there were times when I wanted to quit. Travelling was hard and my identity was frail. Being the role of MANAGER developed personal strength and self-worth. But the process of getting there was tumultuous. Every time my buttons got pushed, I thought, "Okay, now this is it. I'm going to quit," and every time, a picture of Amma would show up. The first time, in Santa Barbara, after a particularly terrible gig, I was moving the pews back into place by myself, grumbling, knowing there was no place for me to sleep that night, feeling no respect, no support, no help. I was coiling cables backstage and someone showed up out of the blue and said, "Please take this picture of my Guru. I think your work is very important. I want you to have this." It was Amma. No one knew I was connected with Amma. Seven months later in Portland, I again came to the end of my rope. Another picture showed up. "Is this a picture of your guru?" I asked. Of course! It was Amma again. My Guru, sending me a message. I wasn't quitting the tour anytime soon. I gathered strength and kept going. A year later, I was running a week-long retreat, getting people registered, setting up the PA system, and it was raining and the students who were tenting outdoors suddenly needed housing indoors, and I just received word that in the middle of the retreat, we needed to fly down to Los Angeles to perform a Hollywood benefit with Seal, and could I make airline reservations... I was overloaded and ready to quit again. I thought, "I have developed self-respect now. I have the stamina. I have a solid identity now. I know what I am made of. I am done." But that weekend, someone gave me a picture of Amma joining two people in marriage. I could feel in my gut that I had to keep going, that my own issues weren't completely worked out yet. I stayed. Four months later at a recording session, I had a disagreement and prepared my letter of resignation. I thought, "Is it over? Am I done yet?" It still wasn't over; we had financial ties, personal ties, tour dates coming up... When our days together finally came to a close, we parted as friends. We are still friends. The friction between us wasn't about him or me. We were just a perfect match for intense personal growth. After I finished managing this artist, a yoga student gave me a large photograph of Ammachi. She was holding armfuls of flower petals to shower on her devotees at the end of the all-night program, She smiled with an incredible mixture of blessing, bliss and exhaustion. This was the last picture I received.

How did I know these were my signals? I sat with them, meditated, and listened. Only you know for sure. No one can tell you what your signs are or what they mean. Do you ask for step-by-step instructions to die? How do you know where to go? You just know. You have to trust that you do know. It's how you got here. It's how you got yourself into your present state of affairs... whatever that may be.

stay present with your own process

What should I do next, Swamiji?

Swamiji: What is in you?

-Shri Shivabalayogi

You do not have to look for your spiritual work. It is right in front of you. It is whatever you are currently doing. It is not what you desire to do; it is not a goal you want to achieve. It is not your life ambition. It is simply what is staring you in the face right now, as we speak. The circumstances in your life are arranged perfectly to create the circumstances for your inner work. You do not have to look for it; it finds you.

External shifts are a result of inner changes. When your internal work is done, your external environment will shift. You will move to a different town, get a new lover, or rearrange your house.

Make your inner world louder than your outer world. Spend time alone. Take a walk. Take a trip. Not sure what to do? Shield yourself from all the advice. Tell your friends and family to give you space for awhile. And then listen. You know exactly what to do. The seed has inside it all the wisdom to become a tree. You don't need advice. Most people just need a practice that reinforces silent space for healing. Your life is already going. Program is running. Your job is just to keep up with it. Processing all the events, surrendering the results, and moving on.

The outer world is always strong. Media, news, gossip, other people's opinions, experts, and media hype present the illusion that something amazing is going on in the world around you. In fact, the only world that matters is yours. Media companies spend billions of dollars just to try to reach "your world," but they're just guessing. The inner world is yours alone. No one else can interpret the signs or understand where it is all leading and where you are going with your life.

Signs, signals, and sensations are experienced internally. Even the physical body is a representation of spirit. Intuitive signals guide you. Follow your hunch. Witness your Self. If you have one awakening, you can trust there will be more.

Move away from knowledge towards inner listening. Write down your feelings. Sit deeply with them and embrace their power. Draw, paint, play music, sing, express yourself. Change your attitude. Be as honest as you can. Self-dialogue is important. Use your affirmations. Change your attitude by affirming to yourself, "I have waited lifetimes to experience this change." Or, "I chose to arrange this experience so I could..."

Surrendering into the experience is especially powerful when you are dealing with physical or emotional pain. There is no way to avoid the pain, so you are forced to dissolve into it. Know that you chose to experience this role in this way, to affect the change most deeply in you. You want to experience it, feel it, live it, so you can know it. As you meditate with pain, you can experience what new perspective it is offering you. This approach is equally transforming with joy, accomplishment, jealousy, and any new change.

You have to show up 100% for the role you are playing. At first it is a matter of just showing up physically. When you show up and participate, all the inner work that needs to be done automatically gets activated. Eventually you will start showing up emotionally, psychically, spiritually as well. All you need to do in the beginning is show up. Perhaps you will be dragged into showing up. Perhaps you will retreat, and recreate the same role in the next situation. That's fine. Might as well get into it.

make your inner world louder

than your outer world

healing crisis

When your spiritual practices change you on the inside, and it no longer matches your life on the outside, you have yourself a healing crisis. Your outer world has to shift in order to align with your heart. Sometimes your karmic ties dissolve or speed up. Things shift before you are "ready," relationships change before you are ready to release them... issues that were hidden inside you suddenly come to the surface. You're in an enormous fight with your long-term partner; you're suddenly saying "I'm not gonna take it anymore" at work... who you are surfaces in a way that surprises you. The events of your life arrange or rearrange themselves to better align with light.

And then sometimes the purification happens very intensely or you get a build-up of spiritual heat (*tapas*) as a result of yoga, chanting, etc., and your life shifts in a bold and explosive way. This is sometimes the only way to make the shift. Sometimes a gradual change is impossible. It is not a science. It is not a sequence. It is often not even logical. It is work of the heart. There is no single way to get there. But many spiritual experiences are similar, and the stories can shed light on how spiritual progress happens.

In the year 2000, I felt as if my heart center were ripping in two, splitting right down the center of my rib cage. It was an unbearable longing which had no medical explanation. During this time I composed and recorded chants to Krishna, often getting up in the middle of the night to sing or record. Chanting to Krishna, I felt a support for this opening. Still the pain did not go away, and I was concerned. The combination of chanting every night, touring heavily, and living my life all had a combined effect of tearing my heart out. It was an alarming, unnerving experience. I decided to record my chants to Krishna. When the day came to record in the studio, I couldn't remember any of the tunes. Everything was 'Hare Krishna'. I had no ideas. I was so absorbed in the energy of Krishna, I was unable to function. I could not command my mind to work. The time? Hare Krishna. My name? Hare Krishna. My schedule this week? Hare Krishna. I had no control over it. It wasn't going to change, it wasn't an energy I could turn off, so I moved forward and worked on the project anyway, and it came out fine. Only in retrospect could I understand this was a reorganization of my mind and spirit. Within a year, the pain subsided and I was reintegrated with myself as a more heart-opened being.

In 1978 I attended a weekend meditation course and came home with a terrible case of hives. The evening I returned home hives appeared under my arms and gradually spread throughout my body. When the hives attacked my internal organs, my breathing became short and I was given the option to enter a hospital for adrenaline shots. I declined and for three days and nights endured states of delirium and cleansing. A fellow ashram student was studying to be a nurse and she attended me night and day, swabbing my body with alcohol. After three days, my body returned to normal. There was no visible cause for the outburst other than the meditation course. This was my first real glimpse of body/mind interconnectedness. It didn't change my physical discomfort. Physical manifestations have to be treated physically as well as psychically. Investigations still need to be done. Medical advice is part of the investigative process.

My teacher put me on silence for one year in 1989. It wasn't a vow of silence like in India, with a chalkboard hanging around my neck. I could talk to people and answer their questions but I wasn't allowed to initiate conversation. No one ever asked me about my life so I could never talk about myself and my problems. It was the hardest year of my life.

What can you do when you're in a healing crisis? Do whatever you can do. Silence can help. Yoga and meditation can help. You will not always be in a position to decide what way is the best. You simply do the best you can.

Spiritual practices cannot change your *karmas*. Your life is a series of experiences you requested when you agreed to take incarnation. What's coming is coming. The difference is, that on a spiritual path, they often come more quickly. The practices are designed to open up who you are, to reveal your true nature. Purification is often necessary to dissolve self-defeating patterns or personality infrastructures which were imposed on you, or which you learned in this lifetime.

When your life needs speeding up, do more yoga, meditation and chanting. If it's too fast, take a break, get a massage or healing treatment. Give yourself time to integrate with the changes your spiritual work has instigated. It has to be in balance. Many years ago in the ashram, we gave spiritual names to our pets, which was a cute idea, except for the fact that their karmas sped up so quickly, they often died unexpected, violent deaths. When we switched back to normal names, they lived pleasant, long lives. It is important to integrate changes and purification into your life at a pace you can handle.

Spiritual practices can speed up your karma. The karmas get fulfilled but faster or sometimes differently than you expected. The relationship you were supposed to have for 7 years is over in 3 years. The fatal accident you were supposed to be in manifests as a fender bender. The spiritual practices offer protection, but the inner work during a healing crisis is far from easy. Purifying requires great courage and diligence.

Maybe it's time to make a change
On the outside, I look the same
But inside my heart I know I'm through
Where will I go? Who can I turn to?
When your world gives way and your heart is rearranged
Will you stick with what you know or will you make a change?
Leap of faith...
How can I leave it all behind
If I don't let go, there'll be nothing to find
Trust the silence and start the day...

research

As your role becomes clear, get as much information as you can about that role. Do research. Find out about as many other people who have played that role as you can. Playing a role may seem superficial. "Oh it's just a role I have to play. It's not really me." In fact it is vital to your growth. You have to play this role. It is essential to igniting the next layer of who you are.

Research what others have done in that role. If you are planning motherhood, research others who have played that role. Talk to relatives and friends, read books. If you are an aggressor, find out about other aggressors with similar missions. Follow how it changed them, how it changed the world. If you are a victim, research others who have been in victim roles. How did they cope, what were the issues, how were they resolved. If you are experiencing a death, find out how others have dealt with the event and process - the initial stages, the options of homecare vs hospital care, the final stages... Find out everything about your role - from physical and practical issues to emotional and spiritual concerns.

And then, very simply: go through the process. Every day, you will be asked to play that role. And every day, you will be pushed to expand the areas that need to be strengthened in you. You chose the role. And you do know how to deal with it. Return to meditation and visualize what playing this role will do for you. Keep reapplying the end result as your intention.

Whatever it is that you are doing now is the result of many lifetimes of preparation. You have been brought to this point in time, to do this particular thing, because you wanted it. It is necessary for your growth. It is part of your karma, part of what you wrote when you arranged your life. This thing that you keep bumping up against over and over is the thing you must master. You know it. The door will keep reappearing until you finally walk through it. Beautiful thing about karma, it will keep repeating in your life until you master it.

Where does your path take you? All doors lead to the same room. We all end up in the same place. How we get there is as varied as the number of personalities out there. That is the incredible beauty of God's Creation. There are so many paths to enlightenment, to self-discovery and inner knowledge. And they all work! You do not have to be anything but yourself to enter the state of bliss. So, the door in front of you is the one you have chosen. It is designed by you and for you. Perhaps you are looking for another door - the blue door with the gold handle, or the *Krishna* door, or the poor poet door, or the fame door, or the intellectual genius door... Look, every door will get you in the room. Select one path and do it; you cannot take all paths at once. From your superconscious, you have chosen this path and opened this door to take you there. It's the perfect thing to push all your buttons, irritate the hell out of you, love you here and back, and make you whole.

intention

your present is the manifestation of your past prayers and longings
your future is the manifestation of your present prayers and longings

Energy follows intention. Wherever you place your attention, your life energy will go there. If you dream of being a star, your energy will go towards supporting that desire. If you are worried that things won't work out, your energy will go towards detailing all the ways it won't work out. The exploration of thought reveals a very powerful teaching: your thoughts direct your energy.

It is therefore a really good idea to set intention, so that your energy flows towards what you want. In Sanskrit, the term is *sankalpa*. Spiritual practices generate a lot of energy; more energy will flow towards you. It's good to develop mind skills to deal with that extra energy. Affirmations and intentions help guide the energy along a positive pathway.

You can set an intention for your yoga practice, dedicating it to yourself or someone in need of the good energy. You can set an intention for your day, your year, your life.

As part of the self-examination process, you become more aware of what you desire. As you determine the outcome of these particular life lessons, you can use the desired outcome as your intention for the relationship or venture.

After meditating, chanting or doing a relaxed spiritual practice, let your mind and heart conjure up the outcome you most desire. What do you most desire in your life right now? Bring it forward into your mind. Feel it. See it. Bless it. And then know this: it has already been set in motion; it is already happening.

Simple and profound, *sankalpa* is a powerful tool.

When you say something with your whole being, not just with your mouth or your intellect, but with your whole being, it can transform the world.

- Thich Nhat Hanh

Practice yoga and purify the body.
Chant divine praises and open the heart.
Sit quietly and meditate in blissful silence.
Spirit lives for this!

CHANTING

singing your heart out

silence

Sound arises out of silence. Yogic texts describe the word Om as encompassing all possible sound - everything that could be said, has been said or will be said. All elements of living expression are contained in the sound Om. Om acknowledges the ever-present silence.

Silence is an energy of consciousness itself. It encompasses all cycles of life and death, every expression and dissolution. Honoring silence, we access the cosmic energy which runs through all living beings, microscopic forms, even giant solar systems. Creating the sound Om, our bodies vibrate with a universal energy, and we align with it. We feel connected; our incarnations become an integral and unique expression of this cosmic energy. Every wave that rises out of the ocean returns and dissolves back into the whole. It is impossible to separate the drops of water from the ocean itself.

Pranava is another name for the *Om* symbol - *prana* is the living energy particles in every cell. *Prana* is the energy that heals, revitalizes, and nourishes. It is especially present in things which are close to the sun – lemons and apples, trees and flowers, you and me. We take *prana* in through food and water, through our hair, through the top of the head (called the tenth gate by yogis), through our lungs and skin. Yoga retains remnants of this worship in the Sun Salutation exercise sequence.

If you are in nature, it is easy to hear the hum of creation – the wind rustling tree branches, the scampering of small creatures, bird calls, the wind in the trees. It is also easy to feel the *prana* – plants carry the bounty of this life giving energy. Surrounded by hundreds of plants, you have a living presence of majestic unfolding.

If you live in a city, you might need meditative assistance to gain the experience of silence. Following the breath, or even increasing the presence of the breath through *ujjayi* breathing (tightening the back of the throat to create a whisper sound while breathing) will help you connect to the ever-present sound of silence.

Silence in this way is not the absence of sound, but the presence of all possible sounds. When you use words, speak, or create a vibration, you are taking the universal energy and creating it into a personal expression. Everything that can be experienced has been done before. Everything you can say has already been said before. You are part of a universal pattern of existence. It is embodied in the sound *Om*.

After every chant there is usually a period of meditative silence. It is a time of surrendering back into silence - the presence of all things, all love and all life. It reminds us that our expressions are part of the universal current.

Creating a sound vibration from within the body makes your energy field whole. Your vocal cords vibrate to create a soundwave; your lungs and diaphragm provide a current of air on which the sound can travel. Because the sound

sound

emanates from within, your body is defined and unified by the sound. Sacred syllables, seed syllables and mantras add potency. By creating a sound from within, you unify your mind and body using your own personal fingerprint: your voice.

When you sing, you create two kinds of sound waves – the sound waves in the air around you and the sound waves travelling through your bones. You hear internally and externally at the same time - through the air and through your bones. External sound waves are the most familiar. Sound generated by your vocal cords creates a wave which travels through the air until it reaches the ears of the person you're talking to. The sound waves are collected by their outer ear, fed through their ear drum and processed by the tiny hammer-like bones of their inner ear. External sound waves travel not only in a straight line but also in random patterns due to the soundwaves bouncing off flat surfaces, making multiple variations, delays and echoes. This gives your voice a certain distinction and fullness.

Internally, the sound has a different quality. Sound waves can travel through both air and water, but the quality of sound travelling through water is muddled. The soundwaves generated by your vocal cords travel internally through your blood, bones, brain and muscle tissue. 98% of your body is water, so the internal sound you hear is similar to being underwater. If you plug your ears and talk, you will get an idea of how it sounds and feels. On your own time, you can submerge yourself in a bathtub and sing to get a more accurate experience. Internal vibrations are potent especially as they relate to in utero experiences. Much of the information you received while being in your mother's womb was through sound and thought vibration. As you create sound through singing and talking, you create vibrations which penetrate your bones, blood, muscle tissue, skull and brain matter.

Both internal and external sound information are needed to speak or sing properly. If you plug your ears and talk, you will hear yourself but an outside listener will notice that your diction is slurred and imprecise. Listen to someone singing along to their favorite song with headphones on; you'll get an idea of what I mean. They won't hit the notes accurately, nor will they pronounce any of the words distinctly. Without external soundwave information, they are unable to make necessary adjustments to make their voice and speech clear.

When you sing, you hear both external and internal sound waves simultaneously. Combined together, you have a complete experience of your own vibration. Most people freak out when they hear a recording of their own singing or speaking for the first time - because they are hearing only the external soundwaves, it sounds funny to them. Is that how I really sound? Yes. But without the internal sound vibrations, your voice will feel incomplete to you. Let's look at internal vibration a little more...

If you put your hands on your chest and sing you will feel your bones vibrating. If you stand in front of the subwoofers at a rock concert, your bones will vibrate also, but that's different. We're not using electronics or amplification here. The sounds you create yourself have special meaning and healing power for you. Your soul knows the sound of your own voice; singing is a form of worship and joyous expression.

Different tones have different effects. Classical Indian music has made a science out of tonality and their healing power. Each tone is associated with a different deity; the notes of the scale are associated with sounds existing in nature, for example the 7th note of a major scale is associated with an elephant trumpet. (Go ahead, record an elephant and see what note it is.) Sound vibration can be used to heal - certain tones held near the afflicted area can eliminate swimmer's ear, break up ovarian cysts, or calm the heartbeat.

For most of us, the last time we heard internal sounds was when we were in the womb. Let's use the ear as a stethoscope and listen to the sound within. Find a partner and place your ear on the back of their rib cage around the heart. We are going to sing *Bolo Ram*. Singers sing and listeners listen. Is it not incredible? Did you ever think the vibrations inside you were so loud? Speech and sound both carry vibration throughout the body, using a combination of breath and vocal chords. Thank your partner and switch places. We will sing *Bolo Ram* again.

I am trying to introduce you to the idea that sound is healing. And there are so many different sounds. The Universe is infinite in its expression. In addition to external and internal sounds, yogic texts describe struck and unstruck sounds. Struck sounds are the ones created by movement, unstruck sounds are created by etheric means. These are overtones, harmonics, hummings in the Universe which exist all the time but which you don't hear all the time. This is music that isn't being played – heavenly music. This celestial unstruck music is called *anahata*. (See meditation p. 118)

You are waves of sound and energy yourself. All energy has a wave form including you. And the molecules vibrate at certain speeds - solids move at a slow speed, liquids at a faster speed, and gaseous or etheric things move at a rapid rate. Human tissue is a combination of all types of matter, so it can vibrate at different speeds. The denser you are, the slower your vibration. The more etheric, the faster your vibration will be.

In chanting, you add a positive thought pattern to the sound wave. Each mantra is an expression of praise or wonderment. With that one expression, you acknowledge that you are not running the Universe. You chalk it up to the Creator - who else could make that beautiful sunset? Who else could take away precious life in an instant? It is all very mysterious and amazing.

Here are some mantras and their translations:

Hare Ram Sita Ram
Ram Ram Hare Ram
Shree Ram Jai Ram, Jai Jai Ram
Opening to Sita and Ram.
Great Ram, Praise Ram
Praise, praise for Ram

Amritamayi Anandamayi
Amritanandamayi Ma, Jai Ma
He Ma Durga, Jaya Jagatambe
Jai Ma
Nectar Mother, Blissful Mother
Nectar Blissful Mother, Praise Her.
Oh Mother! Goddess!
Praise the Mother of the World.

Radhe Bhaj Govind (Radhe)
Radhe Bhaj Gopal
Radhe! Radhe! Radhe Gopala!
Radhe sing of Krishna (Radhe)
Radhe sing, Gopis sing
Radhe! The lovers!
Everyone is in love with Krishna.

Hare Krishna Hare Krishna
Krishna Krishna Hare Hare
Hare Rama Hare Rama
Rama Rama Hare Hare
Opening to Krishna, opening Krishna
Krishna, Krishna, opening, opening
Opening to Rama, opening Rama
Rama, Rama, opening, opening.

Om Namah Shivaya
I bow to Shiva,
the bestower of blessings
and great auspiciousness.

Lokaha Samastaha Sukhino Bhavantu
May all beings in the world find peace.

Om Mani Padme Hum Hrih
May all beings live in Peace

Om Tare Tutare Ture Swaha
Praise Green Tara, Mother of all Buddhas!

lyrics

If this was pop music, you'd be singing the words, "Sing to *Ram*, Sing to *Ram*." Kind of thin, lyrically, don't you think? It's supposed to be thin. When you listen to a good pop song or folk song or rap song, it engages your emotions. Chanting is not designed to do that. You're just singing *Bolo Ram*. How can your mind have much to say to that? How can it respond? *Ram! Ram!* There's nothing there but *Ram*. Contrast that with, "The lotus flowers were blooming so beautifully in the night. I strung a garland of tears around my neck as I waited for You in the moonlight." That's completely different. Oh yes, you are all totally engaged now... Wow, who was that? Who wrote it? Such beautiful images. Who was she waiting for? Actually it is a poem about Krishna, Radha waiting for Krishna.

Chanting is simple lyrically. It's designed to be thin. The more active your brain gets, the more trouble you get in. Really. I am not kidding. As you chant *Bolo Ram* you invoke Divine energy. You invoke it and apply it to who you are. In the beginning, your brain fishes up some things – whatever it is you're working on. It's different for each person. You see, we are all in this room singing *Bolo Ram*, but one person is over here thinking, "Who is she going out with and why?" She is on that channel. Another person is over there thinking pensively, "How exactly does the inner spiral work? Is it these muscles, or those muscles…"

Each thought lasts only as long as it holds energy and every thought has a different lifespan. So you'll think about something until it is no longer entertaining, and it disperses. Next thought comes... Part of the process of chanting is sorting through all the thoughts and being able to look at what's inside your head and heart. By the billionth *Bolo Ram*, you might get to know yourself a little bit.

It's a deprivation in a way. Your tongue can't say anything but infinite words, so the mind is led to infinite thoughts. You are not allowing yourself to speak anything but *Ram*. It's part of *pratyahar*, withdrawing the senses from worldly activity. The tongue is saying only *Ram*. You may be thinking many other thoughts, but eventually there is only *Ram*. Deprivation is a necessary part of spiritual work. It reduces you to the necessary path. It carves out clear channels of energy. Deprivation purifies the mind. When you chant, you are not allowed to say anything but praise. You are on a mono-diet of *Ram*. *Ram* is a very expansive energy. It carries the whole universe. It could be the sun, or *Krishna*, whatever. You're drawing pure energy through your body. That's what creates the change. You start to feel peaceful and happy, because of what's flowing through your body. If it were food, it would be very pure food. Pure intravenous deities.

Chanting is a sealed loop of energy. It's not conversation. The energy recycles and purifies. With lyrics like this, how much conversation can there be? *Sita Ram Sita Ram*. It's sealed. The thoughts don't escape. They sit with you until they purify, dissolve or break for lunch. As they recycle, it creates a heat. It's called *tapas*, which means light or fire. The inner heat purifies your heart and mind.

deities

When you go and ask for a *mantra* from a teacher, they often ask, "Who is your favorite deity?" They give you a *mantra* based on that lineage. Just in case you end up asking for a *mantra* from a saint or guru, I will give you a brief overview of deities. A heads-up, so to speak. (Actually, the fun is in getting lost. Crying out in the middle of a crowded room, "I don't know anything! What do you mean, deity?")

The trinity in Indian philosophy is *Brahma, Vishnu, Shiva.* Generator (*Brahma*), Organizer (*Vishnu*), Destroyer (*Shiva*). Out of *Brahma's* navel cord all creation is born. *Vishnu* arises from *Brahma's* navel, manifesting in various incarnations – *Ram* and *Krishna* are the most well-known. The *Vishnu* deities and *mantras* give sustaining energy. They are like food and love, well that's what it feels like to me. If you need sustenance in your life, those are the *mantras* for you – *Hare Krishna, Shree Ram Jai Ram Jai Jai Ram* – these are great. It helps sustain you in your incarnation. Not trying to open any new energy or create anything new, just trying to sustain what you have. Sustaining and nourishing this incarnation. Sustaining in a beautiful way what you already have.

Shiva is the destroyer. Perhaps it is harder for Westerners to think of worshipping something which is destructive. But if you think of it in terms of destroying impurities – that is what the destruction is for. *Shiva* is not going into destroy *you*. *Shiva* will destroy those aspects of you which are imbalanced and impure. Okay, sometimes it feels like destruction. When you suffer the death of a loved one, or you lose your job or your marriage falls apart, it can feel like you are the one being destroyed. *Shiva* energy is powerful. Things can and do fall apart, especially when you are doing spiritual work.

The female counterpart of *Shiva* is *Durga.* She rides a tiger; she is ferocious and fearless. Her daughter is *Kali.* She's Mother Nature, holding the thunderbolt. "You don't *mess* with Mother Nature!" Do you remember that commercial? *Kali* is just like that. You start messing with Her, She will let you know. In the same way storms come through and correct pollution and rebalance the ecosystem, *Kali* marches through our lives. New life springs from the ashes of the old.

Besides the trinity, there is Ma or Divine Mother, and some people add a separate category for *Ganesha.* And some add a category for *Hanuman*, the monkey god who devoted himself to *Ram.* Everything is worshipped and everything has a place. Each God has a female counterpart, a goddess. Even the music, the ragas, have male and female aspects; *ragas* have corresponding *raginis.* It's all a gigantic system, and we're in it. We have friends and family. The deities have wives and consorts. Most deities have multiple names which correspond to their various aspects. *Krishna* is *Krishna, Gopala, Govind, Devakinandana... Durga* is called on with *Kali, Chamundi, Ambika...* It can be complicated. There is *Brahma's* consort *Saraswati* – beautiful, inspiring. They are all aspects of God, aspects of loving kindness. Don't worry too much about it. Chanting the Names of God will uplift you whether you know the meaning behind it or not.

choosing a mantra

So, perhaps you don't have a guru or teacher you can ask for a *mantra*. How do you choose a *mantra* for yourself? Start with what you are attracted to naturally. I went through a year of just chanting to *Krishna*. I got started chanting it and then I couldn't stop. It was so freeing. I had been in a very disciplined tradition which did not explore the heart. My heart was hardened. The *Krishna* energy came in and opened up my heart. It was such a new experience, I just wanted to hang out there.

The energies from these deities are appropriate at different times in your life. You may stick with *Ram* year after year, but you may not. You don't have to be a die-hard fan. There are no allegiances. It's all good. You should stick with one *mantra* or tradition long enough to know what it has to offer. And only you know how long that is.

And then your life will change. At a time when you are experiencing loss, it might be good to tie into *Kali* or *Shiva* chanting. It might be appropriate at a time when you are trying to process tremendous amounts of grief. "How in the world am I going to process this?" It's too much. Go to the source. *Durge, Durge, Durge Jai Jai Ma.* If life is going to rip you to shreds, you might as well honor the force at work. Worship it, dive into it, understand it, let it renew you.

There are different ways you can apply the energy of the deities to your life. If you want to select a *mantra*, you can look at your life and think about what energy is needed in your life at that point. Are you trying to create something new? *Brahma.* Are you trying to flower what you already have? You may want to sustain your yoga practice, or keep your yoga center and classes going - *Ram* is the one for you. You have a vision, a seed, something that hasn't manifested yet - chant to *Saraswati.* Let the vision come into reality.

You will be naturally attracted to one over the other. You'll hear a *mantra* on a CD and you'll call a friend and say, "Wow, did you hear that *Om Namah Shivaya* chant?" They will not feel the same passion. It's your attraction to the *mantra* that should guide you. If you are attracted to it, sing it all day long.

> *Kirtan should come to you naturally, through your soul... You should sing devotional music in a way that stirs the heart, in harmony and with a slow rhythm. Whenever you make music, singing or playing, it should leave a memory on the mind. Whatever you do, wherever you are, repeat the name of the Lord... It is like nectar, feed everyone with this nectar...*
>
> *- Baba Haidakhan*

Ganesh for removing obstacles. *Ganesha* chants are often done at the start of projects and musical programs. *Ganesh* opens doors.

Brahama and *Saraswati* are for starting things. They are the source of creation.

Ram and *Sita*, *Krishna* and *Radha* are for sustaining and nourishing existing relationships, projects and businesses. To me, chants to these deities are like food, very nourishing and sustaining.

Krishna for unending love.

Lakshmi for money and wealth.

Shiva and *Kali* for embracing what's falling apart and for new beginnings, the phoenix rising out of the ashes kind of thing. These deities create undisturbed energy for diving deep into meditation or solitude.

Divine Mother for whatever you need from the beautiful divine mother.

Hanuman for unleashing supreme devotion, enthusiasm and power.

A celestial sage named Narada was a loud singer who loved to sing sacred songs on his journeys across the heavens. He always carried a veena, a sitar-like instrument which hung from his shoulders, and he liked to think of himself as a fairly skilled musician. One day he came upon a group of extraordinary beings in the forest who were writhing in agony. Narada asked them the cause of their suffering. The creatures said they were personifications of various ragas (musical modes) and were being tormented by Narada's inept renditions of their form. Shocked and awakened by the deep impact his music had on their spirit, Narada promised to study further before singing or playing music again in a haphazard manner. This was very well and good, but the ragas beings still needed to be healed. Someone had to sing the ragas with skill and perfection, and caress and soothe the raga beings back to life. A concert had to be performed. But who would play? Narada needed to find someone capable of healing through sound, with perfect skill and tenderness of heart. Such a perfect musician could only be Lord Shiva. Shiva of course had no reservations about giving an impromptu concert, but for his perfect music, he needed a perfect listener who could appreciate and grasp the subtle nuances of his delightful renderings. Thus he requested Brahma and Vishnu to be his audience. They readily agreed. As soon as Shiva struck his first note, the ragas started healing. It had a visual affect on his divine listeners too. Identifying totally with the soft and melting notes of Shiva's symphony, Vishnu actually started melting himself. Noticing this, Brahma scooped whatever liquid dripped from Vishnu and deposited it in his water pot (kamandalu). From this he delightfully fashioned a beautiful girl. This maiden, because of the auspicious circumstances of her birth, was especially refined herself, and she purified everything she came in contact with. She was Ganga. The Ganges river is named after her, and she flows from the Himalayas into Northern India, healing all she comes in contact with.

what are you saying?

Your mind might be thinking just about anything when you chant. There is no way to control the mind every moment. It goes where it goes. You think what you think and you feel what you feel. You observe what is present in you. To be at peace with it all is the trick. The simplest way to quiet the mind is to slow down the breath. Chanting extends your exhale. And really I can think anything I want while I am chanting, because my body is singing and vibrating "Praise!" "Omigod, I'm alive!" *Jai Ram! Jai Ram!* It doesn't matter what I'm thinking, my mind and body are constantly singing praise. It trains the mind to turn in that direction.

Every tradition has a favorite *mantra*. You go to the *Hare Krishna* ashram, and instead of saying, "Hey, how ya doin'?" they say, "*Hare Krishna.*" The appropriate answer to that greeting is not, "I'm fine" but "*Hare Krishna.*" Why bother with formalities? The main idea behind the practice is opening to something infinite. If you have an experience of openness in a yoga class, you take that experience and try to apply it back into your life. Chanting is the same process. If you lose yourself in a song, in an experience, or in a mantra, you try to find a new way to be open to your life. As you re-enter your world, you participate in a new way.

What are you saying when you sing these *mantras*? Hare means to open, *Krishna* is love. You're saying, "I open to love. I am open to this love." You can say it any way you want. You can just say, "Praise." These are expressions of amazement. Isn't it true? Don't you feel amazed at the way your life is developing? Are you not speechless at the wonder of it all? It's perfect in the way its working on you. Could be good, could be bad. It's still amazing. You fell in love? Wow. You lost your life savings? Wow. It's unexplainable and precisely what you needed to change your heart. What else can you say, except "Wow!" Praise. Praise that which is behind it all.

This life is not something you can create by yourself. There are a lot of forces here at work – divine and human. There are certain lessons you signed up for in this lifetime. Things will go well. You are supposed to experience the beauty of being alive. There are times of happiness and great joy waiting for you. And things will also go very very wrong – you'll go bankrupt, you'll get divorced, there will be bad days - that is also part of what awaits you. For a spiritual person, the bad times are the times of intense growth. Good times are like a ride – you pay the entry fee and enjoy the ride. Bad times, well, they let you see what you are made of. The *mantra* helps you open to what is. You're having a good time right now? Apply the *mantra* and drink deeply of this experience. You're having a bad time right now? Apply the *mantra* and surrender deeper into who you are. If you meet someone after going through a hard experience, you can see the depth in their eyes. You know they've gone through something very real. There's a lot of growth in those bad times. The good times give you hope that all that inner work was worth something. Inner work is constant practice. The good times let you enjoy; the bad times let you see how far you've come.

I remember going to see a master when my life was in shambles. I was balling my eyes out and he was smiling. "Ah this is very good. Very nice." "No you don't understand…" I tried to explain my situation. "No I understand.

This is very very good. *Karmas* are moving." He saw a lot of inner growth and had no care at all about the outer form. It's a different perspective.

We open to all of it. Whatever's coming is coming. When the hard times come, that's great, you will grow so much. When the good times come, that's great, you can feel hopeful and feel the beauty of being alive. We only get two hours together, that leaves twenty-two hours unaccounted for. You have to carry the experience with you, it has to resonate. It has to make sense to you. You can draw on the memory of this experience when you return home. When you chant at home, you will notice immediately how you feel. You can compare it to the memory of how you felt here or how you felt in the presence of a master. Using the memory of the experience as a touchstone, you can set your standard for what you know is possible for you. And yes, it is very, very open.

And very relaxed too. It's not something to achieve; it's something you evolve into. The masters I have met are so easy going, it feels so cozy with them. I thought an enlightened being would have an air of importance; after all, they have gone through austerities and hardship to attain enlightenment, a momentous achievement. But no. They are natural and delightfully present. It feels at once like they are everywhere.

Being with an elevated being changes your mood. It's like getting a message on your answering machine, "Hey, it's Ma calling, just to see how you are doing." Divine presence is available all the time. The trees know it. Everything in nature is aware of this divine vibrating energy. It's what keeps everything alive. It's the beauty you feel when you go into nature. But even if you are in a train station or some urban area, the divine presence is there. For me, it is this energy that is my mainstay, more important than food. If I don't have divine energy, I go mad. I use the mantras to connect to this divine energy and feed myself.

Yogaville, VA - August 2005

three domes

You have three domes in your body. The domes look like upside down bowls, or cathedral ceilings, or archways. Each dome has a special part to play in the creation of sound in your body. The three domes are: the diaphragm, the roof of the mouth or upper palate, and the top of the head. The diaphragm regulates air flowing through the vocal cords, the tongue strikes the upper palate which sends positive messages to the brain, and the top of the head (or tenth gate) regulates the inflow of meditative energy, prayer and blessings. Combined, these three domes activate the chant experience.

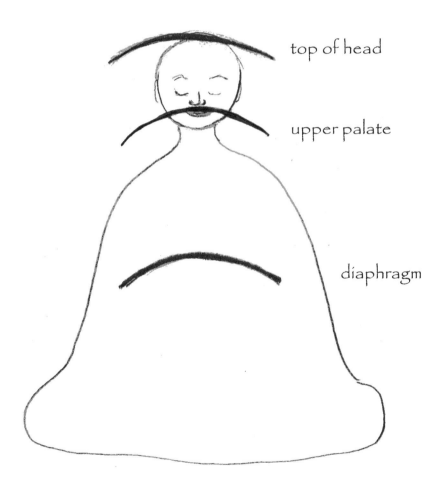

top of head

upper palate

diaphragm

diaphragm

The first dome is the diaphragm. When the diaphragm is relaxed, it is dome-shaped. As you inhale, it flattens down and as you exhale, it rounds up into the body cavity. As you breathe in, your diaphragm flattens out and puts pressure on all those organs, so they are stimulated to work. That's what digests your food. That's why aerobic exercise is so good. Your stomach, liver, all your organs there near the diaphragm get massaged by the breathing process.

As you chant, you use the diaphragm to draw in the breath. *Jai Ram!* You need breath to create that sound. You fill the lungs with air and cry out to your god. It's not a silent meditation. You use your body and your breath to engage yourself in the process. Your breath is vital; with it, you know you are alive. Without food, you still live. Without drink, you can still live. Without thinking, you live. Without breathing, you die. So, that's your connection, through the breath. Through the diaphragm.

To familiarize you with the diaphragm we will practice 4-part breathing with hands on the rib cage, including breath retention on both inhale and exhale. We will then emphasize the inhale by practicing *shakti bhanda* (see p. 48), and emphasize the exhale by practicing *agnisara dhauti* (see p. 27).

Sound is vibration. What creates the sound of your voice? The breath moves over the vocal cords and vibrates. The vocal cords are like two rubberbands in your throat. Let's find the vocal cords, or Adam's Apple, in the throat. Take two fingers on either side of the Adam's Apple and move it back and forth about 2 inches to either side. Yes, it looks weird, it even feels weird. You should know there is nothing permanent in there. It's all muscle tissue holding the parts together.

The vocal cords make tiny adjustments to change pitch. It's like two rubberbands placed side by side. The tighter the rubberbands are, the higher the pitch. The looser they are, the lower the pitch. Your vocal cords make very small adjustments; it's really much less effort than you think. Let's do the motorboat (see *brahmari pranayama*, p. 26). Press the lips together and breathe out through pursed lips, allowing the lips to vibrate as you exhale. Add a song or sound and pretend you are driving a race car, switching gears and tones as you go. Just have fun. It will make your face and sinus area all tingly. That's great - more bloodflow to the face is healthy.

If your lips won't vibrate, you're not giving enough support - use more air and engage the diaphragm, press the lips harder together. This exercise is used by singers to increase awareness of the breath and diaphragm. Sometimes you don't realize how much air you actually need. You sing or speak solely from the throat and run into problems after extended use. This exercise trains singers to engage the diaphragm and use a steady stream of air.

upper palate

The second dome is the roof of the mouth, the upper palate. If you know something about the languages from India, Sanskrit and others, you know that there are dental consonants and retroflexive consonants. The tongue strikes a different part of the upper palate in each type of consonant. They have many more letters in their alphabet than we do. There are four different T's – t, t retroflexive, th, th retroflexive. Same with D's and N's and R's. There is a diagram on the roof of the mouth - different areas of the upper palate correspond to different areas of the brain. So as your tongue hits the front of the palate near your teeth, it's a different effect than your tongue hitting the center of your upper palate.

The tongue attaches at the throat, connecting into the central vagus nervous system. Using the tongue stimulates the nervous system, which might be why some people talk too much! Hearing the sound of your own voice is pleasing to the soul, but in addition to that, the tongue stimulates the nervous system. When I speak to you, my tongue hits my upper palate in a random pattern to create words which convey meaning. During chanting, the tongue hits the upper palete in a repeating, rhythmic pattern. *Hare Krishna Hare Krishna Krishna Krishna Hare Hare, Hare Rama Hare Rama, Rama Rama Hare Hare* - my tongue hits my upper palate 22 times in a steady rhythm. This repeating pattern is soothing to the brain. It releases endorphins, sends a morse code to the brain, saying "Everything's allright."

Place your tongue in the center of your mouth. Now make a suction as you pull the tongue away from the upper palate. It makes a water sound. Sit with your spine straight and hold the mouth open. Just move the tongue. Create a suction. As you pound the upper palate, you will feel the tongue's connection to the brain. Do this for about 4 minutes and then rest.

I'm just doing all these tongue exercises so you don't take notes... just kidding. (laughter) What do you need to know? You already know all this. I'm just reminding you of the obvious. The throat *chakra* is a very powerful *chakra*. The energy starts in the first *chakra* and creates connection through the second and third. Through the heart center, the energy integrates. Through the throat, your projection comes forward. As your projection becomes more refined, you naturally come into music. Many of the saints and sages in India were poets or singers. It's considered a refinement of the incarnation.

Now circle the tongue inside the mouth, placing the tongue in front of the teeth and behind the lips. Make as wide a circle as you can with the tongue. Go clockwise. You'll think it's fun for about 90 seconds, and then you'll feel like your head is going to explode. I'm just warning you, so you don't freak out when it happens. Your ears will burn, your head will hurt as your nervous system is awakened. Don't worry, your head won't explode. If it hurts, just stop for a moment and rest. When you continue the pain will resurface. What is it? It's your nervous system waking up. Nerve damage is painful to repair. Don't worry it's just an introductory exercise. We won't do it for more than a minute or two in each direction. Then inhale and exhale, relax the mouth and nurse on the tongue (swallow the saliva like milk).

Upper palate is a beautiful thing. The sound you create actually resonates in the upper palate. Opera singers try to focus the sound in the sinus area above the upper palate.

We are going to hold a sound in the upper palate and listen to it. It is called **brahmari mudra.** You can sit on a bolster or cushion and bring your legs into a squatting position. Resting elbows on your knees, block off your ears with your first fingers, or place your fingers on your head and block off the ears with the thumbs. It is important that the jaw be slightly open. Create a soft humming noise and listen. Relax the back of the throat and listen to the sound you are creating. Behind the first sound is a second sound. Find it and tune into the second sound. Behind the second sound is a third sound. Tune into the third sound more than the first two. And continue like this for 10-15 minutes, finding as many auditory layers as you can.

At first you will only hear your own voice. It will not be easy, but if you relax you will hear a second sound. I usually hear some kind of harmonic tone from the original sound. Eventually, during the inhale, I notice that a sound is continuing which I am not even creating. When I first heard it, I thought my daughter had connected to the internet and left the speakers blasting, but when I unplugged my ears, the noise was gone. After a few minutes of humming, the noise returned.

These layers of sound are an introduction to *nada brahma*, the original sound of creation, according to Vedic scriptures. You may or may not hear these etheric sounds; it doesn't matter. In the beginning, listen to the vibration you are creating, just like you listened to the vibration by putting your ear on your partner's rib cage.

I have practiced this lying down to relieve migraine headaches. Even if you fall asleep during the practice, you will sleep peacefully. I have also practiced this in the bathtub, submerging my head in the water so I don't have to hold my ears. The seated posture is easiest for regular practice.

three domes

The third dome is the crown *chakra*, what is known as the "soft spot" on a baby's head. Your skull has sutures in it. Maybe you have seen this. The sutures are little finger joints, hairline fractures in the skull which allow the skull to shift or compress while passing through the birth canal. These same finger joints are seen at the Sacro-Iliac joint, where the pelvis joins the spine. The sutures allow the pelvic bowl to expand during labor.

A newborn's head is not fully formed. There is a spot on the top of a baby's head that is totally soft, devoid of skullbone. It's a total freak-out if you are not prepared for it. You go to touch the baby's head, and there's nothing but skin there. And brains. Totally freak you out. From a yogic point of view, that soft spot is the gateway. It's called the 10th gate. That's the gateway between your body and the universal energy of the cosmos. The yogis try to keep that gateway permeable. I used to work on construction sites for awhile, and it was such a great experience because I had been in an ashram doing meditation my whole life and suddenly I was working side by side with beer-guzzling construction workers. I was like, "Wow!" because their 10th gate was like a brick. And I realized, "All right. The world needs bricklayers too." But if you're doing spiritual work, you're trying to keep that gate permeable. You're trying to maintain a connection to the cosmos. To a yogi, that is a very important gateway.

Many people who report on near-death experiences talk about a guiding light or tunnel of light which guides them back to the spirit world. In the same way, there are sounds which guide you back to the spirit world. Some describe it as celestial songs or angels singing. Others describe it as the sound you hear when standing underneath a large electrical power line. Still others describe it as a humming of many tones at once, as if every tone in the Universe were being played at the same time. It is a harmonious, beautiful sound, one that I can only presume has many harmonics and overtones present in it.

We will do a meditation to hear the unstruck sound. It is simple and enjoyable, and has my personal guarantee attached. I have never had a student who could not hear the ringing overtones. I was surprised when I asked a group of students to describe what they had heard - one person heard a ringing phone, another heard the Las Vegas slot machine signalling a win, another heard metal scraping metal, another heard the conch-like sound of the ocean. What will you hear when you hear the unstruck music? Let's find out.

Come sitting with your right leg bent, right elbow on right knee. Place your left foot next to your right foot, either bringing the left ball-of-the-foot or left heel into the instep of your right foot. Cup the right hand under the right ear, nesting the flesh of the thumb under the earlobe where the jaw meets the ear. Keep the right palm open to heaven. Use the left hand to support you in any way you want. It should feel comfortable. Chant *Ma* in a monotone, pausing to inhale whenever you need to. Continue for 5 minutes and change sides.

What are you hearing? They are overtones, always present but we don't always hear them. My experience is that it does something to your brain as well. Not one person has ever had a question after we do this meditation. Everyone is happy and content. I think the sound we hear must heal and soothe the brain. Even though we don't hear all these tones when we chant, they are present. These sounds contribute to the healing and meditative quality of the chant process.

anahata meditation

So, when you're chanting, you can notice all these things - your breath moving in and out, your diaphragm moving up and down, your tongue pitter-pattering on the upper palate, and your 10th gate opening through meditation. All three domes are engaged when you chant.

Let's chant. *Bolo Ram………*

chanting in today's world

What we do is called *japa.* It's repeating. I sing a line, you sing a line. It's not as complicated as classical Indian music; it's not even as intricate as *bhajans* (Indian folk songs). It's just repeating, back and forth between you and me. There's another word called *simran*, which describes the constant flow of sacred vibration. We make a lot of noise doing this chanting; it's true. But what we're trying to do through all the joyful noise is activate a current of sacredness.

The gross, earthly sounds – rock and roll, advertising, everything of the earth – are naturally louder and denser. Things of the earth weigh more. Things of spirit have no weight. They are more delicate. If you put earthly items and etheric items on either side of a scale, the earthly things win every time. It's just the way it goes here on earth. Through the use of amplification, we increase the weight of the sacredness. When that sacred current is activated correctly, you don't need a CD player. It will play all day long in your head.

If you chant in the very early morning when the earthly energy is asleep, the sacredness will be very strong. All normal activities have ceased, your friends are sleeping, it's quiet. No one broadcasts advertisements or news in the middle of the night; there's very little earthly activity. Spirit energy is therefore easier to access. If you play your *mantras* in the early morning, they will remain in your psyche. *Shri Ram Jai Ram Jai Ram Jai Ram Jai Ram.* It will simmer all day. So it is with *simran* – it continues through the 24 hours. This is the energy frequency we try to activate through our practices.

After all, it's hard to be a spirit in a predominantly earthly world. Most spiritual people retreat into caves or live in the woods. They live somewhere removed from society. If you weigh spirit against earth, the earth will always be louder, wealthier, flashier, and more invasive. "Hey man you gotta come over, we got this great garage band, get yourself over here, have a few beers." And "*Sita Ram Sita Ram Sita Ram.*" It just doesn't match; they are different vibrations. They vibrate at different rates. People who are serious in their spiritual pursuit go into a more reclusive atmosphere so the sacred strains can be heard, felt and experienced. Hence, the reason for ashrams, retreats, mountains, caves, and reclusive spots in the world.

But not all of us have that opportunity. The renounced (*sannyasi*) lifestyle is rare. Most of us live as householders, carrying spiritual aspirations while living an earthly existence. If you live in the modern world, you can use amplification. Get some really nice speakers and blast the *mantras*. Crank it up. Amplify the sacred. Do what you can to encourage the sacred frequency in your life.

It's a technique I forgot about til recently. I was complaining to a friend about staying in hotel rooms and feeling depleted by construction noise and overall vibe. I felt like I was awake the whole night in meditation, cleaning up unfinished subconscious garbage from people who had used the room before me. I woke up each day more exhausted. It was really a problem. My friend reminded me, "Don't you play the *mantras* in the room when you get there? Auto-reverse on the speakers. When you get there, put the *mantras* on and leave the room. When you come back, everything will be fine." The CD's set the *mantra* frequency in the room so it became available to me. I had forgotten. That was actually how the CD *Savasana* was used when it first came out – people said it was the perfect Feng Shui CD. They played it in an empty room and came back to enjoy the beautiful vibration.

As it is outside, so it is inside. The mind is the same as the hotel room. The analytical mind is always there first with all its different thoughts, criticisms and comments. It's there first, before *Sita Ram*. As we chant, the balance shifts. By the end, *Sita Ram* is more present than our individual thoughts. And there's more spaciousness. Love is a practice of allowing the presence to work. Love is almost impossible with all our thoughts cranked up. It requires some space to feel it. Love is present all the time just like *simran*, continuing the 24 hours.

We use the word *Jai* in our chanting. *Jai* means 'wow.' It's a form of praise. *He, Jai, Jaya,* and *Wah* are all words which express this amazement. When something happens and you see God's hand in it, you say 'Wow!' What else can you say? Speechlessness is how we acknowledge that God did it, that it was His Hand that created what you see. When we think that someone else created it, we have a lot to say – critics, improvements, meetings. When we realize it was an act of God, then who says anything? How can it be debated? Does anyone gather together to discuss the improvement of the position of the moon in the sky? No. We see it as an act of God. When the moon comes up, people look in the sky and say, 'Wow!' It's so beautiful. What else can be said? Should be a little more to the left? No. It's appreciated as God's unexplainable presence in our lives. And so it is with you. The only difference is whether you see the hand of God in your life or not. We practice saying *'Jai Ram'* or *'Jai Ma'* as a reminder that this unseen Hand is present in everything we do and experience.

We're looking for a constant experience of it. *Mantra japa* is one of the easiest ways to get there. Sitting in silent meditation following your breath is somewhat harder; it requires more skill, more concentration. In silent meditation you must examine each thought. When all thoughts are released, you get to silence. With *mantra japa*, by the end of your practice, every thought turns into the repetition of the *mantra*. You are left only with *Sita Ram Sita Ram*, or whatever your *mantra* happens to be. It all turns into this sacred thread. With the *mantra* blaring in your ears, you cannot escape the repetition. The repetition naturally draws you into a meditative, introspective state.

When your mind is finally one – everything is *Jai Ram* – then you experience the silence. It kind of rings in your ears. This silence is not an empty thing; it is not the absence of sound or the absence of thought. It's the all-inclusive presence of one sound, the sound of *Om*, the sound of nature, the hum of machines, of babies being born and people dying. This hum is the universe working - it's active. Some call it presence - presence of love, of silence, of enlightened masters, of all *mantras* repeating at the same time. At first, it's *Jai Ram Jai Ram Jai Ram*, and then it's *jairamjairamjairam* and then its *jairamramramramramramraaaaaaaaaaaaaaaaaaaaaam*, then *Om*. One *mantra* turns into many *mantras*, which turns into *Om*, or the sound of every *mantra*. There are no individual thoughts here, only the presence of one thought.

If sacred music fills the hall, room or the car you are in, then no matter what activity you are doing, the sacred vibration is present. This is the beauty of amplification; it exaggerates the presence of the *mantras*. No matter what you're doing – shopping, cleaning the house, chopping wood, washing vegetables, driving – the energy hums through you. Even while talking to someone else, the vibration continues. It's amplified. It is continuously projected by the mind. This is such a beautiful thing. In our modern world, the *mantra* enters our hearts from CD's and live music and continues until it repeats automatically and silently within.

Mountain View, CA - August 14, 2004

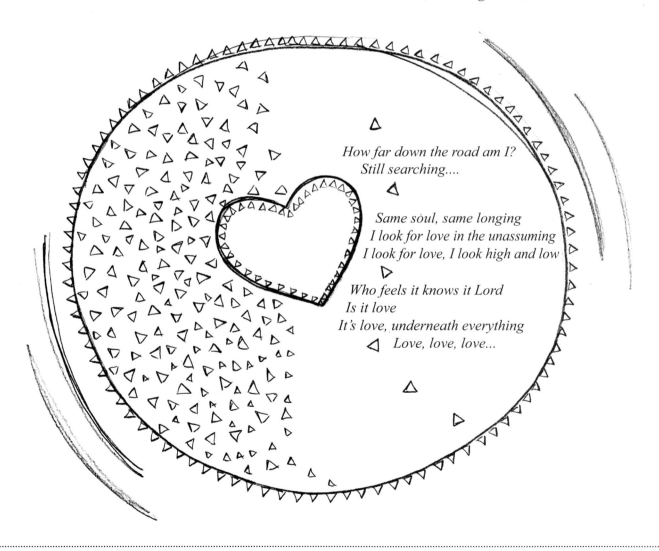

How far down the road am I?
Still searching....

Same soul, same longing
I look for love in the unassuming
I look for love, I look high and low

Who feels it knows it Lord
Is it love
It's love, underneath everything
Love, love, love...

all night programs

(after an all-night chanting program)

This chanting that we do creates light. It's energy. It travels from mind to mind. It doesn't obey time and space. It can travel from this side of the world to the other. It concerns matters of the spirit. Spirit doesn't have any weight. The earth has lots of weight – media, advertising, bars, parties, making money – all these things that are earthly are dense. Their speed of rotation is slower. As you move into the spirit world, there's no weight.

It doesn't look like anything to a normal eye. This event is an event of spirit. It starts in an empty room, it ends in an empty room. You didn't drink any brews, you didn't make any money. So what did you do?

It's etheric. It has a buoyancy. It rotates at a faster rate. The higher *chakras* rotate at a faster frequency. In the comparison between the two, earth wins. When I was a teenager, I went to a healer and he said to me, "You are like a silk cloth. What happens when you drop a brick on a silk cloth?" I thought about that image for a minute. He said, "Try to remember - you're not burlap. You need to treat yourself differently." The fabric of who we are as we get more buoyant, is lighter. It has different frequencies.

Living in LA, there are lots of partiers. When I go for my morning walk, I see the recycling bins overflowing with empty wine and beer bottles. I shake my head and wonder, "How can they consume all that?" And they shake their head when they see me, "How can she just sit there and meditate in a room like that?" They are different frequencies.

When you stay up all night and exaggerate the spirit frequency, the energy of the sacred silk thread gets amplified. Not just from the music, but from our experience. It becomes bigger, more prominent in who we are. Everyone I've met today, I can only say, "Hey…" It's the only word that describes our shared experience. It's a word of praise. You know? "Hey…" We might have been fighting the night before, but today, it's like, "Hey…" That's why they call it the night so beautiful (*rain so bhai*). In the battle of the frequencies, the spirit wins. An all-night *kirtan* allows the higher frequencies to dominate, in an otherwise earth-dominated world. Or, shall we say, in an otherwise earth-glutted life. I speak for myself. I need a dose of it on a regular basis. It's been like this since I started chanting, age 17, maybe even younger. I must have an experience of spirit, or I will no longer understand why I am here on earth, being tortured in a resurrected body on this *karma*-pit called earth, or however you describe feeling crazy and out of place. As a young person, I couldn't deal with the earth frequencies being so strong. Some of us come in very etheric, I was one of that type.

As a young person, I couldn't deal with the balance between the frequencies. Earth seemed so strong and heavy and, well, like the thing to do. I felt (and still do) that the maya was real. Making money, making connections, having a business, networking – I felt that all of that was real. I take it very seriously even now, like I have to do my emails, and I have this feeling like I really need to participate in this earth thing.

But then after I have chanted for awhile, I look at the earth and its value disintegrates; it no longer holds up. The earth is like sugar. It's very sweet and tastes so good. But when you add the water of the Name, it disintegrates. The sugar dissolves. All of a sudden, I see the earthly problems as nothing at all.

I have trouble distinguishing between what's real and what's not real. Someone comes before me, I see them and think they are who they are. I see their clothes, their level of wealth, importance. After chanting for some time, I see them and say, "Hey…" I only see their light. For me, I need to see the inner side more. It needs to be exaggerated for me to feel happy, to feel cozy. Otherwise it feels like the healer said, like my life is a brick tearing through my sacred self.

I'm game. Let's come back every weekend. Isn't it true? Today, you are seeing only the light. Everyone you see, you say, "Hey…" You have a shared experience.

Sleeplessness is part of it. When you have sleep you can keep it all together. If you have your sleep and your normal pattern of activity, then who you think you are is right there. The teachers can't get to who you are when you have all your guards up. They mess with your mind; they ask you to go and start a business in Tokyo. What?! All of a sudden you are in Tokyo. You're off-guard; you're vulnerable. Who you are comes forward. The teachers ask us to do things we have no skills for. On purpose. It's a technique to mix you up, turn you into a tossed salad. Once you are scrambled, your false impression can crumble and your real self can come forward. Who you thought you were was all nicely put together, and then the moment your teacher asks you to do something odd – for example, standing in a tree for three days – then, how you think the world is put together just shatters. At that moment, it's like you are the sugar and they just poured a bucket of water on you! Everything that is illusion gets washed away.

Sleeplessness is a technique. The Tibetans use it. You go on retreat in a cave, you sit in a box, you are not expected to sleep. If you fall asleep in the box, you're going to bonk your head on the wood encasing. As you stay up, the boundary between earth and spirit becomes transparent. You don't know – are you sleeping? Were you awake? When you're sleeping you're hearing the music. When you're awake, you're kind of zoned out. It changes your boundaries. It's such a help. Really. We all have our lives put together somehow. You can't grow if it stays that way. So you have to be drenched every now and again. Drenched in the Name, you are freed of some of your patterns.

At the end of the all night programs with Ammachi, they get bowls and bowls of rose petals. We circle around and She throws handfuls of petals at us, showering us with blessings as we run under Her gaze. After that's done, She stands there and holds the petals in both hands. Have you ever seen the pictures of Lakshmi, the goddess of wealth, with the gold coins dripping out of her hands? OK, just remember we've all been up all night, just like now. Those petals dripping out of Her hands are like liquid gold dripping from Her hands. And She looks like she's going to pass out. There's so much spirit there, you wonder when you look at Her, "Is this the last moment of Her life?" Like She's not going to be able to come back. There's so much spirit, you think there's no way She's going to come back in Her body this time. She's already travelled that path so many times, She's in between worlds. She takes a long time as She stands there with rose petals dripping from Her being. It's been many hours of chanting and blessing. The energy feels like it does right now – very spacious and open. The energy seeps in. Everything is disjointed, the boundaries are very transparent. And in our in between state, we can absorb spirit energy. It is the same here. As we sit here, there is abundance of spirit energy that can seep in easily. It's so special.

Someone asked Mother how She stays up all night. We stayed up one night; Amma stays up every night. I'm thinking I'll try it once a week; I'm being conservative. The all-night programs go every 4 days or so. Someone asked her how She does it day in and day out. She replied, "Enthusiasm." When I heard that, I was like, "Yeah!" I could feel the energy of that statement. When you put the energy out, it comes back at you. I have a friend who is a healer. He says all he really does for a living is love people. That's the whole process.

The closing prayer we sing says, "May I be led from untruth to truth. May my laziness change to inspiration, my giving-up and hopelessness change into a willingness to experience and seek out bliss. May all beings experience peace. May they experience perfection in their lives, and may the music resound in their minds long after this gathering has ended."

Om asatoma sat gamaya
Tamasoma jyotir gamaya
Mrityorma amritam gamaya
Om shanti shanti shantihi
Peace and happiness to all beings.

Om sarvesham svastir bhavatu
Sarvesham shantir bhavatu
Sarvesham purnam bhavatu
Sarvesham mangalam bhavatu
Om shanti shanti shantihi.

This whole thing is infinite. But when you are on the earth, you want to find it in finite form - you want to build a foundation, find a niche in the market, take a course, read a book, learn a system. You want to see the steps, how to do it. I'm telling you, there is no right way to live a life. If there were, someone would have made millions by now selling their patented formula. Tell me, is there a step-by-step process for sunrise? Can you say, "OK, first step: silence. Then, a few birds. Hey! Not yet! No birds singing yet, not until I give the signal!" You can't do it. The process of Creation is a combined leap into infinity. I can't explain it to you, you can't explain it to me. We come together and share our stories and our lives. We can witness it together and share this moment...

Omega Institute afternoon - September 2004

Q: Why do harmoniums have such a unique sound?

WAH!: Probably because they are out of tune. (laughter) No, I'm serious. The harmonium has several rows of reeds. Each reed is made individually. No two are reeds are exactly the same. This creates a variance in tone and pitch. When one note is played, several reeds activate and it creates a variance or fullness, or sometimes slight dissonance if it's out of tune. And in some cultures, for example in Bali, they purposely tune the instruments to be dissonant with each other to create beats of sound. It induces trance.

Q: Do you do continuous breathing when you chant?

WAH!: No, just breathe as you need to. Look, chanting and yoga are supposed to be simple. They are for us common folk, not for the elite. It used to be something that only ordained priests could do. You had to have correct bloodline and belong to a *Brahman* family. There were qualifications you had to meet to be able to lead prayers. This chanting that we do is very very simple. It doesn't require great talent. It's something that anyone can do at any time to improve their situation.

I try to keep it as simple as possible, so people's brains don't engage. That's why I didn't want you to take notes. It puts me in my brain, which isn't good for either of us. You can go a long way with intellectual knowledge. Long way… "First we will learn *Sa Re Ga Ma.* And then, when you get to *Ma*, we will learn a meditation. But first, you must do some *karma* yoga, sweeping floors to clear your mind and *karmas*. Then you can receive the initiation. I will teach you *Sa Re Ga* and you can come back in few months and we will see. Maybe I will be able to teach you *Ma*." (laughter)

But this is the tradition! There is no paper. Have you ever tried to carry around a book in India? Oh my God! One monsoon season, you will not have your book any longer. Pages are growing mold, the binding is broken, half the pages are ripped out by accident, some pages went out the window when you were on the bus and were eaten by a wandering cow who mistakenly ate it with some grass on the side of the road…. How can you keep a book in India? You can't. This is why everything is oral tradition. It is just from me to you. That is the beauty of it. It's not what you read in a book, it's "what did you discover?"

Your students will only go as deep as you can go. As far as I have gotten in my practice, I can share that with you. You can experience it through my vibration. If I meditate with you and I have reached a certain level in my meditation, you can experience that. That is why some of us run around like madmen looking for saints to meditate with. In their presence, we experience a new level. "Wow, it's not like this at home" I think to myself as I compare the two experiences. Because they have achieved a certain level of expertise in their spiritual practice, they bring me to it when I am in their presence. Some people teach in this manner, all teaching done in silence through meditation. The more you know, the more you can share. It cannot be described. The more evolved you are as a soul, the more people are going to be able to experience through you.

Q: How do you evolve?

WAH!: You practice. You experiment and find what works for you. Do you think these practices dropped out of the sky? No, they were developed. In the Himalayas, the yogis escaped their towns and gathered to practice and experiment with the techniques. They refined their experience, documented the best ones. They meditated and practiced and developed all these techniques we have today. And then they kept them secret. Most of these practices were kept hidden from public view. They're just not given out freely to anyone who wants them. Normally, you would have to go to a cave, meet someone, bring them some food, and maybe, *maybe* you would receive one of these morsels. That's the tradition, and I believe it should stay that way. It's a person to person thing. Your teachers are offering you information, knowledge and an experience which you will pass onto others. With the internet and books, a lot of knowledge can be gotten; but it's the experience that's special; it is something shared between two people. That is the real thing.

Every time you see someone, you should ask "What did you find out?" You will be surprised what people are going through. If you find inspiration, share it with someone. When people come to your classes, they are not coming for the knowledge. They can get that anywhere. There is so much knowledge in the world, you could drown in it. What I am giving you today is a little morsel. What you will get from someone else is a different morsel, equally valuable. But you need to come to the understanding that you will never learn it all, not even in several lifetimes. So give it up. We keep coming back, incarnation after incarnation, until we get it all learned. You will probably not finish this lifetime.

Q: What happens when your throat gets sore when you're singing?

WAH!: You're probably trying too hard. When you first go up into handstand, you use more muscles than you actually need. Right? So, when you first start singing, you use all kinds of muscles that are unnecessary, and perhaps you are straining in that way. Singing is just prolonged, sustained talking. Some people think when they sing, they have to push more air than they actually need t

Q: Do you warm up before you sing?

WAH!: No. I don't warm up before singing. I don't warm up before meditation. I don't even warm up before yoga. That's probably why I do an invocation! (laughter) Let God take care of it.

epilogue

The Universe is an interconnected web of people helping other people. Each of us carries someone along; each of us has someone who is depending on us to care for them – our children, our family, a co-worker, a person on the street. We grow through being there for them, helping them, giving them love and nurturance. In the same way, there is always a being higher than you willing to help you forward. It's an interconnected web; there's always someone below and above. We help each other.

The teachers at the forefront of yoga, chanting and other healing modalities have been cared for and molded by their teachers. They are continuing a long-standing tradition of personal relationship between Guru and disciple. Perhaps it isn't named that way in so many words but the transfer of light continues from teacher to student, from healer to healed, from counselor to patient. The world is a network of so many lightworkers.

Some people publicize their lineage and encourage others to find what they have found; others keep their Guru and disciple process as a personal and private privilege. Still others have amalgamated their process and define their teachers as Source itself. These are all so many names for the same thing. Source flows through our teachers to us or flows directly to us. The transfer of light remains the same.

We evolve by participating in the process. As teachers we learn to hold and integrate more light and become more effective healers and helpers. As students we learn what is possible for our own lives and how we can integrate more healing into our families, relationships and lifework.

So don't feel that you have to create something – a style of teaching, or a new yoga center, or a change in your job or relationship. You don't have to do anything. Just show up and offer yourself wholeheartedly to the process. As the energy mixes with who you are, a flow is established. It naturally leads you to what you should be doing. We don't create these healing technologies; we participate in them. It changes us, and that's a real privilege.

All energy gets recycled in new forms; all matter is recreated. Our enthusiasm to embrace the work before us gives us access to infinite sources of healing energy.

Light energy is shared and passed down from person to person, heart to heart. It reveals itself in every interaction. An experience of personal friendship gives rise to a sense of community. It includes not just the people in your immediate surroundings but those you meet coincidentally. We have a global community with many different traditions and lineages all mingling together. Each tradition was started with one act of kindness, one person helping another. Let's keep passing it on.

Now that I have tasted bliss
I want it day and night.
Your caress still lingers on my face.
Your music fills my sleep.

Oh this ache in my heart!
I walk the ocean's depth in search of you.
All day I create gifts to give you
Hoping today I'll see you face to face.

I tread a narrow ledge
Between endless sky and earth below.
I move slowly so I can enjoy your love
And search the source of this nectar.

My guides have told me this:
Drink the nectar a thousand times
And it will still never be enough!
Touch your fingertips to the edge of grace
And be at peace.
Love is endless.